GW00691312

AS Chemistry
UNIT 2

OCR

Salters

Module 2848:
Chemistry of Natural Resources

Ashley Wheway

Philip Allan Updates
Market Place
Deddington
Oxfordshire
OX15 0SE

tel: 01869 338652
fax: 01869 337590
e-mail: sales@philipallan.co.uk
www.philipallan.co.uk

© Philip Allan Updates 2003

ISBN 0 86003 749 5

All rights reserved; no part of this publication may be reproduced, stored in a retrieval system, or transmitted, in any form or by any means, electronic, mechanical, photocopying, recording or otherwise without either the prior written permission of Philip Allan Updates or a licence permitting restricted copying in the United Kingdom issued by the Copyright Licensing Agency Ltd, 90 Tottenham Court Road, London W1P 9HE.

This guide has been written specifically to support students preparing for the OCR Salters AS Chemistry Unit 2 examination. The content has been neither approved nor endorsed by OCR or Salters and remains the sole responsibility of the author.

Printed by Information Press, Eynsham, Oxford

Contents

Introduction

■ ■ ■

Content Guidance

■ ■ ■

Questions and Answers

Introduction

About this guide

This guide is designed to help you prepare for the second OCR (Salters) A2 chemistry unit test, which examines the content of **Module 2848: Chemistry of Natural Resources**. This module is divided into three sections: **From minerals to elements**, **The atmosphere** and **The polymer revolution**.

The aim of this guide is to provide you with a clear understanding of the requirements of the module and to advise you on how best to meet those requirements.

It is not intended as a last minute crammer, nor does it contain all the material you need to be aware of. However, it does cover the facts and main 'chemical ideas' that you are required to know. During your studies, you will acquire much more information, which may help to improve your extended-writing responses.

The guide is divided into the following sections:
- This **Introduction**, which provides guidance on study, revision and examination techniques, showing you how to prepare for the unit test.
- **Content Guidance**, which provides a summary of the facts and chemical ideas introduced and developed in Module 2848.
- **Questions and Answers**, in which you will find questions in the same style as in the unit test, followed by model answers. Examiner's comments follow these answers. Careful consideration of the answers and comments will improve your:
  — understanding of the chemistry involved
  — examination technique
  — score in the examination

To understand chemistry, you have to be able to make links between chemical ideas. The Salters course gradually develops concepts through the different storylines. This approach leads to the continuous revision of chemical ideas. The first AS module consolidates and develops ideas from GCSE, as well as introducing new concepts and principles. It is important to make sure that your understanding of GCSE and the ideas in Module 2850 is secure, before developing them further. A brief reminder of this prior knowledge is outlined at the start of each topic in the Content Guidance section.

The specification

The specification is not an optional extra to be looked at as the examination approaches. It is an essential component of your study materials throughout the course. It is much more than a document to tell teachers what they should be teaching and students what they should be learning. It outlines the format of the modules and contains details of the chemical knowledge and the depth of understanding you need to achieve to succeed. There is advice about a number of issues, such as:

- the correct ways of writing formulae
- details of what is required in the 'open-book paper'
- guidelines for success in the practical assessments

If your teacher is not able to provide you with a full copy of the specification, it can be obtained from OCR for a small cost. It can also be downloaded from the web at **www.ocr.org.uk**

A word of warning: OCR (Salters) chemistry has its own study materials — the *Storylines* and *Chemical Ideas* books and worksheets. In revising, you need to distinguish between what the specification says you *must* know and the extra information contained in the Salters materials. Your own notes, taken in class and enhanced through personal study, should be restricted to the specification guidelines and should be your main resource for revision. The most important contexts from the three 'storylines' of this module are covered in the Question and Answer section of this guide.

The unit test

The unit test is a structured question paper of duration 1 hour 30 minutes, worth 90 marks. It counts for 40% of the AS or 20% of the A-level marks.

The unit has two assessment objectives. **AO1** is knowledge with understanding. This means you can be asked to:

- recall and recognise specific facts. For example, 'What colour is an aqueous solution of bromine?' or 'What is the name of the functional group circled in the formula above?'
- recall laws, principles and concepts and be able to understand how to apply them to examples given in the specification. For example, 'State Le Chatelier's principle. Use it to explain the effect on the acidity of seawater of increasing the carbon dioxide concentration in the air.'
- know the meaning of specified terminology and be able to use the words correctly when referring to the examples studied. For example, 'Give the formula of the nucleophile in the reaction between bromobutane and aqueous sodium hydroxide.'
- recognise, recall and understand the following practical techniques:
  - extracting and washing a liquid organic compound using a separating funnel
  - purifying an organic liquid and measuring its boiling point using fractional distillation
  - making up a standard solution
  - performing an accurate titration
  - vacuum filtration

AO2 is application of knowledge and understanding, analysis and evaluation. This means you could be asked to:

- describe, explain and interpret chemical phenomena and effects using chemical principles and concepts, presenting arguments and ideas clearly and logically, using the appropriate specialist vocabulary. For example, 'Describe and explain the effect on the yield of ammonia in the Haber process of (a) increasing the pressure in the reactor and (b) increasing the temperature of the reaction.' (The Haber process is not in the specification for the module. Therefore, you will be given more information from which you must select the relevant ideas to use in order to answer the question.)

- interpret and translate data from one form to another. Data may be presented as continuous prose, tables, diagrams and graphs. For example, 'Draw the skeletal formula of chlorobutane. Use the enthalpy diagram for the decomposition of hydrogen peroxide to comment on the enthalpy change for the reaction.'

- carry out calculations. Those mentioned in the specification involve:
  — concentrations of solutions
  — titrations
  — determining oxidation states of atoms in compounds and ions
  — the use of the equation $E = h\nu$
  — composition by volume, measured in percentage concentrations and in parts per million (ppm)

  Calculations are an integral part of chemistry at AS and A2. Therefore, some types of calculation met in Module 2850 could be tested here, including:
  — using the 'mole concept' to determine masses of substances and volumes of gases
  — empirical and molecular formulae
  — percentage composition

- apply chemical principles and concepts to unfamiliar situations, including those related to the responsible use of chemistry in society. For example, you should be able to look at a flow diagram or equations for an industrial reaction sequence and be able to describe and explain possible environmental issues involved. Given appropriate data for gases, you should be able to comment on whether they might lead to global warming, ozone depletion or acid rain.

- assess the validity of chemical information, experiments, inferences and statements. For example, 'Are Ziegler–Natta catalysts true catalysts? Are they not really initiators?' You should be able to point out problems with a given experimental procedure or set of apparatus.

In AS unit tests, two-thirds of the questions are AO1 type and one-third AO2.

Command terms

The following command terms are often used in Salters examination questions. You must be clear what you are being asked to do.

Describe — tell the examiner about... This could be about a reaction, the properties of a compound, how to carry out an experiment or the results from an experiment.

Explain — use chemical ideas to say why and how things happen.

Suggest — give a *possible* example, technique or reason.

Using — you must make sure that whatever the examiner wants you to use is referred to in your answer.

Classify — assign examples to a particular group or category.

Complete — usually a table, diagram, sentence or formula.

Draw — this used to apply to drawing chemical apparatus as two-dimensional sections. Increasing use of IT has made this largely a forgotten art. However, you should be able to recognise apparatus, spot errors and suggest possible improvements to such diagrams. 'Draw' also applies to constructing structural formulae. Make sure that you know how to draw full formulae correctly for the examples in this unit.

Preparing for the unit test

Preparation begins when you start the AS course. The end result, the unit test, is designed not only to show the examiner what you know and understand, but to show that you can organise information and communicate facts and ideas clearly and logically.

Reading

I give my students a weekly planner that tells them what each lesson covers and indicates the necessary prior reading from *Storylines* and *Chemical Ideas*. This reading enables the lesson time to be used effectively. Students will have noted points that need further clarification and sometimes areas that do not make *any* sense! As we discuss each topic, the students make connections quickly and develop an under-standing more easily.

It is not easy to fit reading into your programme, but it provides a big bonus for those prepared to make the effort. You should make sure that you know what is coming next. With the Salters course, there is no excuse for not finding this out.

Note-taking

The use of loose-leaf paper is often unsatisfactory. Pages are lost for a variety of reasons or can rearrange themselves at will. I favour the use of hard-backed notebooks, using one side in class and leaving the opposite side for follow-up work and revision comments.

You should scan-read your lesson notes the day they are made, to check for errors. You will have forgotten the details of the lesson if you leave it any longer. Remember, these notes are for revision and should be easy on the eye as well as concise, clear and accurate. You will need to include some information from *Storylines, Chemical Ideas,* the Salters worksheets and your own research. Make them a labour of love. You will need them if you continue to A2. You should ask your teacher to check them.

Study groups

Studying in groups is an important way of learning. You could form a group that meets regularly to sort out ideas, read each other's notes, prepare practical work, go over errors made in tests and talk through some of the more difficult exercises.

Revision

When the time comes for revision, do:

- have a plan — I like the idea of 'revision bytes', i.e. small chunks of material easily assimilated in a short period of continuous activity
- revise regularly — if you work in fits and starts, you will have difficulty retaining information
- test yourself — write the essentials on scrap paper
- meet your study group — test each other

Past papers

Past papers are an important resource. You could do some under examination conditions and use others as a resource during revision on specific topics.

The examiners' mark schemes and reports are also important. The mark schemes give information about what is and what is not acceptable for each answer. Your teacher should have copies of these or you can obtain them from OCR. The examiners' reports give details of where students did well and also of areas where students generally need to improve. These documents form a valuable student resource.

Storylines

In the 48 hours before the unit test, you should read through the relevant *Storylines* and take note of the assignments. This will remind you of the scope of the module and bring the contexts to mind. Also, the assignments often contain the types of question that appear on the papers.

During the unit test

- Make sure you look at the *Data Sheet*. It has a copy of the periodic table, which is an important resource. Make sure that you know how to use it effectively.
- Before you pick up your pen, *read the whole question paper*. This is important for two reasons. First, it allows you to select which question to begin with; this might not be the first question. Decide which question you will find the easiest and gain

confidence by scoring heavily at the beginning. Second, while you are working on one question, the subconscious part of your brain may trigger helpful thinking for a different question.

- Now *read the question carefully*. Highlight or underline important command words and data given. As you cover each part, check the mark allocation. Have you made enough points? Have you shown your working in a calculation? These issues are covered in the Question and Answer section of this guide. By the time the exam comes along, they should be second nature to you.

- Answers that require extended writing should be planned in rough first. You will have time to do this. If you do not have any paper, you will find space in your answer booklet. Examiners decide what is an appropriate space for your response. If your writing is large, you may need a little more space; if it is tiny, you will not need to fill it. Make sure that you are not rephrasing the question or using it as an introduction to your reply.

- The Unit 2 test has 2 marks for 'quality of written communication'. These are usually referred to as QWC marks. Both marks are awarded for pieces of extended writing. One of the marks is for writing two sentences in which there is no more than one spelling, punctuation or grammatical mistake. Some students write solely in capital letters — they will not gain this mark. It is also important that your writing is legible! The second mark is for organising relevant information clearly and coherently, using specialist vocabulary.

Content
Guidance

This section is a guide to the content of **Module 2848: Chemistry of Natural Resources**. Unlike the specification for this module, the material is arranged under chemical topics rather than the three *Storylines* contexts. These topics are:

- Atomic structure and the periodic table
- Structure and bonding
- Competition and precipitation reactions
- Group 7: the halogens
- Calculations and moles
- Organic chemistry
- Photochemistry
- Chemical equilibrium
- Rate of reaction

The essential facts are largely in tables or diagrams for easy access and revision. There is also guidance about specific chemical ideas and issues.

Do take note of the 'prior knowledge' sections that head each topic. These remind you of the knowledge required from GCSE and Module 2850: Chemistry for Life, which is assumed in this guide.

Answers to the questions appearing in this section are on pages 46–48.

Atomic structure and the periodic table

Prior knowledge

It is assumed that you know:

- the electron structure of the first 20 elements in terms of shells and energy levels
- how to label shells using n, the principal quantum number
- the meaning of the term 'ground state'

Sub-shells, orbitals and conventions for representing electrons

Atomic spectra of the elements show that electron shells are split into **sub-shells**. Sub-shells are labelled s, p, d and f. Different sub-shells can hold different numbers of electrons. The sub-shells themselves contain **atomic orbitals**.

At AS and A2, we associate orbitals with regions of space around the nucleus in which the electrons are moving. Although we can measure the energy that an electron has, we do not know its actual position. We only know the *probability* of finding an electron at a particular position in an orbital.

Each orbital can hold up to two electrons. Electrons in orbitals can be thought of as spinning either clockwise or anticlockwise. If two electrons are present in an orbital, they have opposite spins.

The table below summarises the information about the sub-shells and orbitals needed to deduce the electron configuration of the elements from hydrogen to krypton.

Principal quantum number (n)	Sub-shell label	Number of atomic orbitals in sub-shell	Maximum number of electrons in sub-shell	Maximum number of electrons in shell
1	1s	1	2	2
2	2s	1	2	8
	2p	3	6	
3	3s	1	2	18
	3p	3	6	
	3d	5	10	
4	4s	1	2	32
	4p	3	6	

Krypton has eight electrons in its outer shell, but shell 4 can contain a maximum of 32 electrons if the $4d$ and $4f$ sub-shells are present.

Orbitals are often represented as labelled boxes and electrons as arrows. The diagram shows this for a $2s$ sub-shell containing two electrons and a $2p$ sub-shell with three orbitals, two of which are occupied by a single electron.

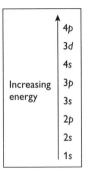

Electronic structure of the first 36 elements in the periodic table

The different atomic orbitals have different energy levels. The order of energy from lowest to highest for the atomic orbitals in the table above is:

	$4p$
	$3d$
	$4s$
Increasing energy	$3p$
	$3s$
	$2p$
	$2s$
	$1s$

Remember that the $4s$ orbital is slightly lower in energy than the set of $3d$ orbitals.

The arrangement of the electrons of an atom in orbitals is called its **electron configuration**. Alternative terms for this are **electron arrangement** and **electronic structure**.

You can work out the ground state electron configuration of any of the atoms of elements from H to Kr using the following rules:
- Look up its atomic number (proton number).
- Add the same number of electrons to the orbitals in order of increasing energy.
- If there are two electrons in one orbital they must have opposite spins.
- If there are several orbitals with the same energy (e.g. p- and d-orbitals), the electrons first go in singly with parallel spins.

The ground state electronic configuration of some of the elements is given in the table below. A shorthand notation is used to represent the electronic configuration.

You should be able to write the electron configuration of the first 36 elements in the periodic table.

Element	Number of electrons	Electron configuration	Comment
H	1	1s1	Only one electron, therefore easy!
He	2	$1s^2$	Electrons have opposite spins
Li	3	1s22s1	Third electron must go up a level
B	5	1s22s22p1	Fifth electron into new sub-shell
N	7	$1s^22s^22p^3$	All three electrons in p-orbitals have parallel spins
Ne	10	$1s^22s^22p^6$	2p orbitals now filled
Na	11	$1s^22s^22p^63s^1$	Eleventh electron must go up a level
Ar	18	$1s^22s^22p^63s^23p^6$	3p orbitals now filled
Ca	20	$1s^22s^22p^63s^23p^64s^2$	Electrons go into 4s before 3d
Sc	21	$1s^22s^22p^63s^23p^63d^14s^2$	3d orbitals fill before the 4p orbitals
V	23	$1s^22s^22p^63s^23p^63d^34s^2$	All the d-electrons have parallel spins
Cr	24	$1s^22s^22p^63s^23p^63d^54s^1$	All the d-electrons have parallel spins; $3d^54s^1$ (half-filled d-set) is more stable than $3d^44s^2$
Mn	25	$1s^22s^22p^63s^23p^63d^54s^2$	Back to normal!
Ni	28	$1s^22s^22p^63s^23p^63d^84s^2$	Two d-orbitals are singly occupied and have parallel spins
Cu	29	$1s^22s^22p^63s^23p^63d^{10}4s^1$	$3d^{10}4s^1$ (filled d-set) is more stable than $3d^94s^2$
Ga	31	$1s^22s^22p^63s^23p^63d^{10}4s^24p^1$	Back to normal again!
Kr	36	$1s^22s^22p^63s^23p^63d^{10}4s^24p^6$	Finished!

Blocks in the periodic table

The elements in the periodic table are grouped into blocks. The first three of these are labelled **s-block**, **p-block** and **d-block**. The outer orbital, which is being filled, gives its name to the block.

Question 1

In which period do the f-block elements first appear?

Structure and bonding

Prior knowledge

It is assumed that you know about:

- giant ionic and covalent structures (GCSE)
- shapes of molecules
- ionic, metallic, covalent and dative covalent bonding
- simple description of intermolecular forces (GCSE)
- alkanes and alcohols
- enthalpy measurements

Relationship between structure and bonding

You need to be able to:

- identify whether particles in a substance are **atoms**, **molecules** or **ions**
- distinguish clearly between the terms **structure** and **bonding**

Question 2

(a) **Make a list of rules that will help you decide what type of particle is present in a substance, given its name or formula.**

(b) **Use your list to decide what type of particle is present in:**

- **potassium bromide, KBr**
- **sulphur hexafluoride, SF$_6$**
- **copper, Cu**
- **poly(butene)**
- **aqueous hydrogen bromide**

You should be able to understand and appreciate the comparisons made in the following table.

Structure	Bonding
The way atoms and ions are arranged in a substance	The type of 'electron glue' that holds the atoms together in a given structure
Can be determined experimentally	A theoretical concept using models to explain how and why atoms form ions and molecules
Types of structure: • Ionic lattice (e.g. NaCl) • Metallic lattice (e.g. Na, Mg, Al) • Giant atomic lattice or network (e.g. diamond and silicon(IV) oxide) • Molecules (e.g. H_2O, Br_2, C_2H_6) • Polymers or macromolecules (e.g. poly(ethene))	Types of bonding: • Ionic • Metallic • Covalent • Dative covalent

Structure	Bonding
Properties affected by the type of particle in a structure: • Ions cause a substance to conduct electricity when liquid or in solution • Ions or polar molecules may make a substance soluble in water • Networks have high melting and boiling points	Properties affected by the strength of bonds: • Weak covalent bonds break easily (e.g. peroxides decompose readily, giving off oxygen) • Very strong bonds make molecules unreactive (e.g. nitrogen gas)

Molecules and network structures

Network is another name for giant. You should be able to sketch the network structures of diamond and silicon(IV) oxide, showing how the atoms are joined together and the approximate bond angles.

In addition, for CO_2 and SiO_2 you must be able to:

- compare their properties
- describe their structures
- discuss their intramolecular bonding
- appreciate the role intermolecular forces play in deciding the properties of CO_2
- explain their properties in terms of their structures and bonding

	Carbon dioxide	Silicon(IV) oxide
Formula	CO_2	SiO_2
Properties	Gas at room temperature; soluble in water	Solid with high melting point; insoluble in water
Structure	Molecular	Network (giant)
Intramolecular bonding	Covalent	Covalent
Intermolecular forces	Very weak	Strong covalent bonds throughout the network

Sodium chloride, diamond and silicon(IV) oxide

The structures and properties of NaCl, diamond and SiO_2 are summarised in the table below.

	NaCl	Diamond	SiO_2
Structure	Each ion is surrounded by six oppositely charged ions — this forms a cubic ionic lattice	Each carbon atom is covalently bonded, tetrahedrally, to four others — this forms a giant lattice (network)	Each silicon atom is covalently bonded, tetrahedrally, to four oxygen atoms — this forms a giant lattice with O–Si–O linkages (network)

	NaCl	Diamond	SiO$_2$
Hardness	Brittle — close, oppositely charged ions repel	Very hard — strong C–C bonds	Hard — strong Si–O bonds
Melting point	High (801°C) — strong net attractive force between oppositely charged ions in lattice	Very high (3820°C) — very strong bonds between atoms	Very high (1610°C) — very strong bonds between atoms
Solubility in water	Soluble — water forms strong ion–dipole interactions with ions	Insoluble — water molecules cannot interact with carbon atoms to break down the structure	Insoluble — water molecules cannot interact with silicon and oxygen atoms to break down the structure
Electrical conductivity	Does not conduct electricity in the solid state — ions cannot move	Does not conduct electricity — no ions or free electrons present	Does not conduct electricity — no ions or free electrons present

Electronegativity, polar bonds and polar molecules

Electronegativity is the ability of an atom in a molecule to attract electrons.

Electron pairs in bonds are not equally shared between the two atoms. If the value of the electronegativity difference between the two atoms is significant, then the bond is **polar**. This means that the more electronegative of the two atoms has a slight negative charge and the other has a slight positive charge. For example,

$$\text{Partial charges} \quad \overset{\delta+}{C}\text{———}\overset{\delta-}{F}$$

Electronegativity values   2.6   4.0

Remember that C–H bonds are considered to be non-polar.

There are two requirements for a molecule to be polar, i.e. to have a permanent dipole:
- It must have at least one polar bond.
- If there is more than one polar bond, the individual bond dipoles must not cancel each other out.

The second point depends upon the shape of the molecule. Consider carbon dioxide and sulphur dioxide molecules. Both have polar bonds, but look at their shapes:

$$\overset{\delta-}{O}=\overset{\delta+}{C}\overset{\delta-}{=}O$$

The dipoles cancel; the molecule is non-polar

The dipoles do not cancel; the molecule is polar

A sulphur dioxide molecule has a negative end and a positive end; a carbon dioxide molecule does not.

Intermolecular forces

The table below summarises what you need to know about intermolecular forces.

	Type of intermolecular force		
	Instantaneous dipole–induced dipole	Permanent dipole–permanent dipole	Hydrogen bonding
Particles it occurs between	All	Molecules with a permanent dipole	Suitable hydrogen atom on one molecule, small electro-negative atom (F, O, N) on the other
Approximate strength	0.1–$1.0\,kJ\,mol^{-1}$	1–$10\,kJ\,mol^{-1}$	10–$100\,kJ\,mol^{-1}$
Example	Propane H—C—C—C—H (with H atoms)	Ethanal H—C—C=O (with H atoms)	Ethanol H—C—C—O—H (with H atoms)
Example	C–H bonds are considered to be non-polar	Permanent dipole due to the C=O bond H_3C $\delta+$ C=O $\delta-$ H The hydrogen atoms are not suitable for hydrogen bonding	Suitable hydrogen atom and an oxygen atom C_2H_5—O: $\delta-$ ··· H C_2H_5—O: $\delta+$ H
M_r of example	44	44	46
Boiling point of example	$-42°C$	$21°C$	$78°C$

Do not use the term van der Waals forces when you mean instantaneous dipole–induced dipole forces. van der Waals forces are a collection of forces and include interactions between permanent dipoles and induced dipoles.

A 'suitable hydrogen' for hydrogen bonding is usually one that is attached to an oxygen, nitrogen or fluorine atom. Sometimes a hydrogen atom attached to a carbon atom that also has several halogen atoms attached is suitable.

Question 3

Trichloromethane and propanone molecules form hydrogen bonds with each other. Draw a diagram to show one hydrogen bond between the two molecules.

Competition and precipitation reactions

Prior knowledge

You are expected to know about:
- formulae of ions (GCSE)
- oxidation and reduction (GCSE)

Redox in terms of electron transfer

Redox reactions are **competition** reactions, in which particles compete for electrons. You should know and understand the following *three* ways of describing a redox reaction.

Oxidation	Reduction
A substance gaining oxygen	A substance losing oxygen
A substance losing electrons	A substance gaining electrons
The oxidation state of an atom increasing	The oxidation state of an atom decreasing

Remember:
- the mnemonic '**oilrig**' applies to electron transfer and *not* to changes in oxidation state (**o**xidation **is l**oss of electrons, **r**eduction **is g**ain)
- an **oxidising agent** *gains* electrons and is *reduced*
- a **reducing agent** *loses* electrons and is *oxidised*

Oxidation states

The **oxidation state** of an atom is best considered as simply a number (with a sign) that can be calculated for each atom in a molecule or ion, using a set of rules. It is a measure of the control that an atom has over its electrons, and can help us decide whether oxidation and reduction are occurring in a given reaction. These rules are also important in naming molecules and ions and in helping to construct redox equations. These last two uses are studied at A2.

Assigning oxidation states to atoms

Some of the rules for assigning oxidation states are summarised in the table below.

Atom	Oxidation state
Free element	0
Group 1	+1
Group 2	+2

Atom	Oxidation state
Aluminium	+3
Fluorine	–1
Oxygen	–2
Hydrogen	+1
Chlorine, bromine or iodine	–1

The following exceptions should be noted:

- Oxygen has an oxidation state of –1 in peroxides (which contain an O–O bond) and +2 in OF_2.
- Hydrogen has an oxidation state of –1 in ionic hydrides (H^-).
- Chlorine, bromine and iodine have higher oxidation states than –1 when combined with oxygen or a more reactive halogen (e.g. in ClF_3 the oxidation state of chlorine is +3).

You also need to remember that:

- in a *compound*, the sum of the oxidation states of all the atoms in the formula is *zero*
- in an *ion,* the sum of the oxidation states of all the atoms in the formula equals the *charge on the ion*

Tip Students often make mistakes in calculating oxidation states where there is more than one atom of the same kind present. For instance, in calculating the oxidation state of Cl in Cl_2O they look at the formula and remember correctly that the sum has to be zero and that oxygen is always –2. They arrive at the incorrect answer of +2, whereas for *each* chlorine atom the answer is +1.

Question 4

Calculate the oxidation state of:
- sulphur in $Na_2S_2O_3$
- nitrogen in NO_3^-
- phosphorus in P_2O_3
- nitrogen in NH_4^+

Tip The term oxidation number is also used at AS to mean oxidation state. Exam papers will use the term oxidation state. You will not lose credit if you use oxidation number.

Proton transfer in acid–base reactions

Acid–base reactions are competition reactions in which particles compete for protons.

They involve the transfer of an H^+ ion (proton) from the acid to the base.
- An acid is a *proton donor.*
- A base is a *proton acceptor.*

$$\text{HCl(aq)} + \text{H}_2\text{O(l)} \longrightarrow \text{H}_3\text{O}^+\text{(aq)} + \text{Cl}^-\text{(aq)}$$
$$\text{Acid 1} \qquad \text{Base 2} \qquad\quad \text{Acid 2} \qquad \text{Base 1}$$

H_3O^+ is the oxonium ion.

In water, a hydrogen chloride molecule behaves as an acid because it gives a proton to a water molecule (the base). The $\text{H}_3\text{O}^+\text{(aq)}$ ion formed can also be written as $\text{H}^+\text{(aq)}$. Note that the oxonium ion is also an acid and the chloride ion is also a base. Acid–base pairs such as HCl–Cl$^-$ and H_3O^+–H_2O are called **conjugate** acid–base pairs.

Water can also behave as an acid. A substance which can behave as both an acid and a base is said to be **amphoteric**.

$$\text{NH}_3\text{(aq)} + \text{H}_2\text{O(l)} \longrightarrow \text{NH}_4^+\text{(aq)} + \text{OH}^-\text{(aq)}$$
$$\text{Base 1} \qquad \text{Acid 2} \qquad\quad \text{Acid 1} \qquad \text{Base 2}$$

Question 5

Suggest a reaction that might occur if a chloride ion were a much stronger base than water.

Hydration of ions in solution

Some ionic solids dissolve in water because the polar water molecules are able to interact with the ions. The weak dipoles on water molecules are attracted to the ions, releasing energy. This energy is sufficient to overcome the attraction between the oppositely charged ions in the solid compound. Ions in solution are said to be **hydrated**.

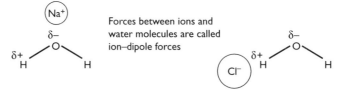

Forces between ions and water molecules are called ion–dipole forces

The average number of water molecules surrounding an ion depends on the size and charge of the ion.

Question 6

Explain why non-hydrated chloride ions are larger than non-hydrated sodium ions.

Precipitation reactions and ionic equations

It is important to remember that ions in solution behave *independently*. This means that, when a solution of ions takes part in a reaction, often only one type of ion reacts. Ions that do not take part in the reaction are called **spectator** ions. This makes it easier to understand what is happening in the reaction and to write the correct ionic equation.

A **precipitation reaction** takes place when two solutions containing ions are mixed and a solid forms.

To write an ionic equation, follow these steps:
- **Step 1**: identify the solid that forms.
- **Step 2**: write its formula on the right-hand side of the equation, followed by the (s) state symbol.
- **Step 3**: write down the formulae of the ions that come together to form the solid, followed by the (aq) state symbols.
- **Step 4**: balance the equation.

Example

Observation

When aqueous sodium hydroxide is added to copper(II) sulphate solution a blue precipitate forms.

Writing the ionic equation

Remember that the positive ion from one solution reacts with the negative ion from the other to form a solid that is insoluble in water.

In this case, the precipitate is either copper(II) hydroxide or sodium sulphate. How can we decide? The precipitate is blue, indicating that it is a transition metal compound. In general, it is worth remembering two solubility rules:
- All group 1 compounds are soluble.
- All nitrates are soluble.

(These rules will enable you to identify the name of the precipitate in any such reaction you are likely to meet at AS or A2.)

- **Step 1**: the precipitate is copper(II) hydroxide.
- **Step 2**: $\longrightarrow Cu(OH)_2(s)$
- **Step 3**: $Cu^{2+}(aq) + OH^-(aq) \longrightarrow Cu(OH)_2(s)$
- **Step 4**: $Cu^{2+}(aq) + 2OH^-(aq) \longrightarrow Cu(OH)_2(s)$

Reactions of halide ions with silver nitrate

You should be able to write ionic equations for the following reactions of aqueous halide ions with aqueous silver nitrate.

Positive ion in aqueous silver nitrate	Negative ion in aqueous metal halide	Appearance of precipitate	Formula of precipitate
$Ag^+(aq)$	$Cl^-(aq)$	White	$AgCl(s)$
$Ag^+(aq)$	$Br^-(aq)$	Cream	$AgBr(s)$
$Ag^+(aq)$	$I^-(aq)$	Yellow	$AgI(s)$

Group 7: the halogens

Prior knowledge

You are expected to know about the trends in group 7 from GCSE.

Physical properties

Property	Chlorine	Bromine	Iodine
State at room temperature	Gas	Liquid (volatile)	Solid (volatile)
Appearance at room temperature	Greenish-yellow	Brown (orange vapour)	Dark grey (purple vapour); crystalline
Appearance in water	Pale greenish-yellow	Orange	Pale yellow (brown in aqueous KI)
Appearance in organic solvents	Pale greenish-yellow	Orange	Purple

Displacement of halide ions by halogens

Halide ions (Cl^-, Br^-, I^-) are colourless in aqueous solution. Therefore, any colour change is due to one halogen molecule displacing another.

If you can remember the colours of the halogens when dissolved in water and their relative reactivity, you will be able to predict and write an ionic equation for any one of these reactions. In these reactions, the *halogen is the oxidising agent* and the *halide ion is the reducing reagent.*

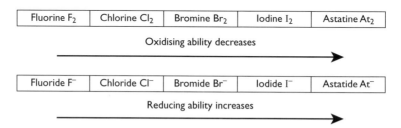

| Fluorine F_2 | Chlorine Cl_2 | Bromine Br_2 | Iodine I_2 | Astatine At_2 |

Oxidising ability decreases

| Fluoride F^- | Chloride Cl^- | Bromide Br^- | Iodide I^- | Astatide At^- |

Reducing ability increases

Question 7

(a) **What will you see when aqueous chlorine is added to aqueous potassium iodide?**

(b) **Write the ionic equation for the reaction between aqueous chlorine and aqueous potassium iodide.**

Calculations and moles

Prior knowledge

You are expected to know how to:
- use the mole concept to perform calculations involving masses of substances
- use the mole concept to perform calculations involving volumes of gases
- construct balanced chemical equations

Setting out calculations

You should set your working out so that examiners can give you credit for knowing how to tackle a given problem.

Whenever you use an 'equals sign', the left-hand side should contain at least one word or symbol that defines the quantity you are attempting to calculate. The right-hand side should not be only numbers and mathematical signs — it should contain the appropriate units.

Concentration of solutions

Equation 1
$$\text{amount of substance (mol)} = \frac{\text{mass (g)}}{\text{molar mass (g mol}^{-1})}$$

Equation 2
$$\text{concentration (mol dm}^{-3}) = \frac{\text{amount of substance (mol)}}{\text{volume of solution (dm}^3)}$$

At AS, calculations are structured. This means that each calculation is split up into steps, each step requiring a different type of calculation or deduction. All the data required are provided in the question. So look carefully at what you have been given!

Example

What mass of sodium hydroxide is present in $100\,cm^3$ of a $0.100\,mol\,dm^{-3}$ solution? (A_r: H, 1.0; O, 16.0; Na, 23.0)

In the calculation, start with the concentration of the standard solution (a solution whose concentration is known accurately) and use equation 2 to find the amount of NaOH in the solution.

$$\text{moles of NaOH} = \text{concentration} \times \text{volume of solution}$$
$$= 0.100 \times \frac{100}{1000}\,\text{mol}$$

Now use equation 1 to calculate the mass of NaOH used.

$$M_r \text{ of NaOH} = 23.0 + 16.0 + 1.0 = 40.0$$
$$\text{mass of NaOH} = 0.100 \times \frac{100}{1000} \times 40.0\,\text{g} = 0.40\,\text{g}$$

Tip
- Most students tend to calculate the relative formula mass (M_r) rather than molar mass. This is fine as long as you remember that M_r does not have units.
- Remember that the volume in a concentration expression has units dm^3, not cm^3.

- Do not use the abbreviations ml or cc.
- Do not use your calculator until you arrive at the last step. This reduces your chance of making arithmetical errors.
- Make sure that you use the correct number of significant figures in your final answer. On every exam paper there is 1 mark for using the correct number of significant figures in a specified calculation.

Acid–alkali titration

You should be able to use a given balanced equation or information about ratios of reacting moles to determine volumes or concentrations of reacting solutions.

Example

$25.00\,cm^3$ of a solution of limewater (calcium hydroxide solution) are titrated with $0.0300\,mol\,dm^{-3}$ hydrochloric acid solution. The titre is $23.50\,cm^3$. Calculate the concentration of the calcium hydroxide in the limewater.

The equation for the reaction is:

$$Ca(OH)_2 + 2HCl \rightleftharpoons CaCl_2 + 2H_2O$$

Start with the concentration of the standard solution and use equation 2 to find the amount of HCl in the titre.

$$\text{moles of HCl in titre} = \text{concentration} \times \text{volume of solution}$$

$$= 0.0300 \times \frac{23.50}{1000}\,mol$$

$$\text{moles of } Ca(OH)_2 \text{ needed to neutralise the HCl titre} = 0.5 \times 0.0300 \times \frac{23.50}{1000}\,mol$$

$$\text{concentration of } Ca(OH)_2 = 0.5 \times 0.0300 \times \frac{23.50}{1000} \times \frac{1000}{25.00}\,mol\,dm^{-3}$$

$$= 0.0141\,mol\,dm^{-3}$$

Tip
- You may find it helpful to write the data given and what you are trying to find under the appropriate substances in the equation. This makes it easier to see which substance is the standard solution. For the above example:

$$Ca(OH)_2 + \quad 2HCl \quad \rightleftharpoons \quad CaCl_2 + 2H_2O$$
$$25.00\,cm^3 \qquad 23.50\,cm^3$$
$$?\,mol\,dm^{-3} \quad 0.0300\,mol\,dm^{-3}$$

- In the second step, you need to refer to the equation for the correct ratio of acid to alkali.
- Wait until the last step to use your calculator. The 1000s always cancel — a useful check!

Volume composition

Two methods are used to state the proportions of each gas present in the atmosphere:
- concentration by volume, expressed as a percentage
- parts per million (ppm), which is used for substances present in small concentrations

For example, carbon dioxide has a concentration in the atmosphere of 367 ppm. This means that in 10^6 parts measured by volume, 367 parts are carbon dioxide. In other words, there are 367 cm^3 of carbon dioxide in $10^6 cm^3$ of the atmosphere.

Expressing this as a percentage by volume:

$$\text{concentration of carbon dioxide} = \frac{(367 \times 100)}{10^6} = 0.0367\%$$

Organic chemistry

Prior knowledge

You are expected to know:
- about structural isomerism and molecular shapes
- the difference between aliphatic and aromatic compounds
- how to recognise the homologous series alkanes, cycloalkanes, alkenes, alcohols and ethers
- about the combustion of alkanes and alcohols
- that simple addition polymers are formed from alkene monomers and you should be able to draw the structure of the repeating unit of a polymer

Homologous series

The homologous series that you need to be able to recognise are summarised in the table. You must also be able to name **alkenes** and **halogenoalkanes**.

Homologous series	General formula	Functional group	Example
Alkenes	C_nH_{2n}	$\diagdown C = C \diagup$	$H_3CHC = CHCH_3$ But-2-ene
Halogenoalkanes	$C_nH_{2n+1}X$, where X is a halogen atom	$—X$	$H_3C — \overset{\displaystyle CH_3}{\underset{\displaystyle Br}{C}} — CH_3$ 2-bromo-2-methylpropane

Homologous series	General formula	Functional group	Example
Aldehydes	$C_nH_{2n}O$	(functional group structure: —C with =O and H)	C_2H_5—C (with =O and H)
Ketones	$C_nH_{2n}O$	(functional group structure: —C with =O and alkyl group)	H_3C and H_3C joined to C=O
Carboxylic acids	$C_nH_{2n+1}COOH$	(functional group structure: —C with =O and O—H)	C_2H_5—C (with =O and OH)

Naming organic compounds

There are three steps to naming an organic compound. A halogenoalkane is used here as an example.

Step 1: identify the longest carbon chain and name it as the appropriate alkane.

The alkane is butane.

Step 2: identify the substituent halogen groups and add them as a prefix, putting the groups in alphabetical order of the halogen. Use di, tri etc. to signify the number of similar substituent groups. Ignore these prefixes when arranging the groups alphabetically.

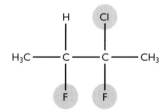

The prefix is chlorofluoro-, so the name so far is chlorodifluorobutane.

Step 3: number substituents from the end of the carbon chain that gives the lowest sum of the substituent positions.

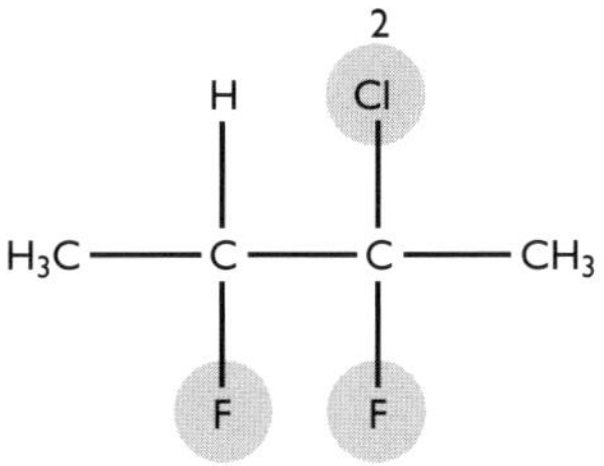

The correct name is 2-chloro-2,3-difluorobutane (not 3-chloro-2,3-difluorobutane).

Alcohols

Alcohols with only one hydroxyl group (OH) are called **monohydric** alcohols. Monohydric alcohols can be classified as **primary**, **secondary** or **tertiary** alcohols.

Type of alcohol	Position of hydroxyl group	Example
Primary	End of chain (attached to a carbon atom which has at least two hydrogen atoms attached)	Butan-1-ol 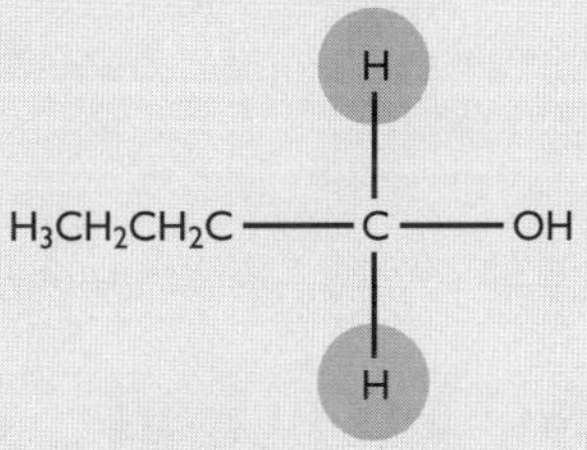
Secondary	Middle of chain (attached to a carbon atom which has one hydrogen atom attached)	Butan-2-ol 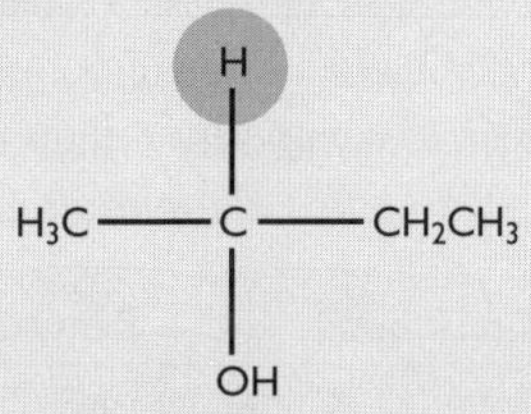
Tertiary	Attached to a carbon atom which has no hydrogen atoms attached	2-methylpropan-2-ol 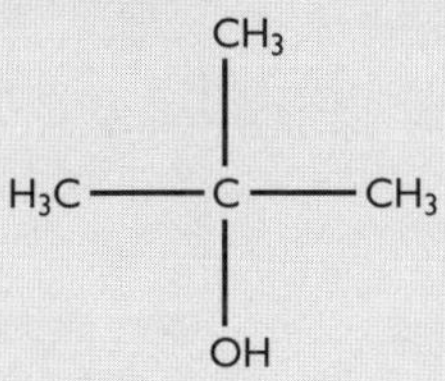

Geometric isomers

These are also called *cis–trans* isomers. Two conditions are needed for a compound to show this type of isomerism:

- At room temperature, there must be restricted rotation about a bond. Single bonds rotate freely but double bonds cannot rotate without an input of energy or the use of a catalyst to break and re-form one of the bonds. The bond which gives rise to geometric isomers most often is the carbon–carbon double bond (C=C).
- There must be two groups on adjacent carbon atoms that can be arranged differently in space — either on the same side (*cis* isomer) or on opposite sides (*trans* isomer) of the double bond.

There are three alkenes that are structural isomers with the molecular formula C_4H_8:

H_2C⸺$CHCH_2CH_3$ H_3CHC⸺$CHCH_3$ H_2C⸺$C(CH_3)_2$

But-1-ene   But-2-ene   2-methylprop-1-ene

There are two geometric isomers of but-2-ene:

cis-but-2-ene   trans-but-2-ene

Question 8

Explain why 1,2-dibromocyclohexane forms *cis* and *trans* isomers.

Reactions to learn

You need to know the reagents and conditions for a number of reactions. Examiners have a variety of ways of asking questions about these. Make sure that you are familiar with the facts about each reaction and how it is used. Some are used to make other substances (synthesis). Others are used to help find out about the functional group present in a substance. Examples are given in the Question and Answer section of this guide.

Compound	Reagent	Conditions	Products
Alkane	Chlorine, Cl_2	Ultraviolet light	Chloroalkanes and HCl
Alkene	Bromine, Br_2	Room temperature	Dibromoalkane
Alkene	Aqueous HBr	Room temperature	Bromoalkane
Alkene	Hydrogen, H_2	Platinum catalyst at room temperature (or nickel catalyst at 150°C)	Alkane
Alkene	Water, H_2O	Phosphoric acid catalyst on SiO_2 support at 300°C and 60 atm pressure	Alcohol

Compound	Reagent	Conditions	Products
Halogenoalkane (RX)	Aqueous sodium hydroxide	Heat under reflux	Alcohol and a sodium halide (NaX)
Halogenoalkane (RX)	Concentrated aqueous ammonia, NH_3	Heat in a sealed tube	Amine and HX (react further to produce a salt)

The oxidation of alcohols depends on the position of the hydroxyl group. These reactions are summarised in the table below.

	Primary	Secondary	Tertiary
Example of alcohol	Ethanol 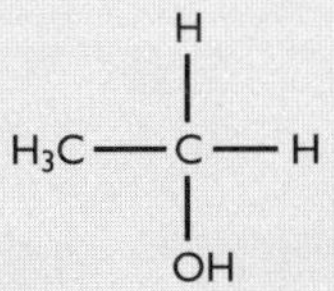 H_3C — C — H with H above and OH below	Propan-2-ol 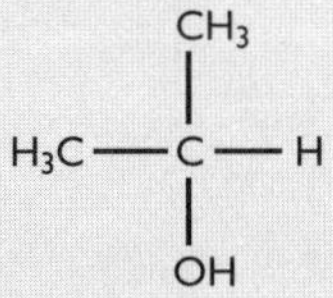 H_3C — C — H with CH_3 above and OH below	2-methylpropan-2-ol 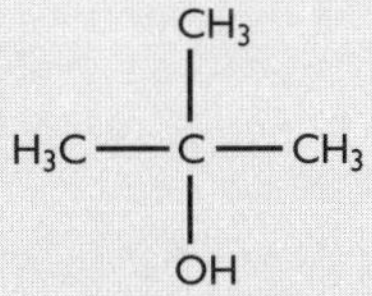 H_3C — C — CH_3 with CH_3 above and OH below
Oxidation product(s)	Ethanal 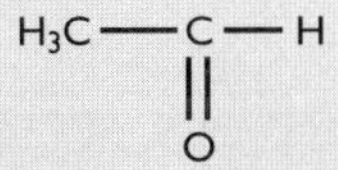 H_3C — C — H (=O) Further oxidation occurs, producing ethanoic acid 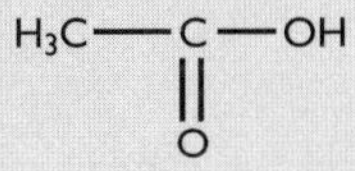 H_3C — C — OH (=O)	Propanone H_3C — C (=O) with CH_3 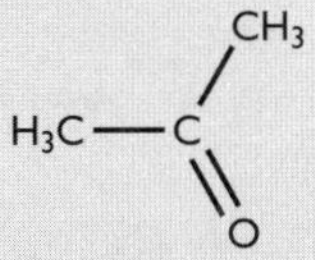	No reaction
Colour change of acidified $K_2Cr_2O_7$ (oxidising agent)	Orange to green	Orange to green	No change

Synthesis of halogenoalkanes from alcohols

There are essentially three stages in preparing an organic compound by a synthetic route involving a single reaction step. These are:

- reaction
- separation
- purification

These steps are summarised in the flow diagram below, using the preparation of 1-bromobutane from butan-1-ol as an example.

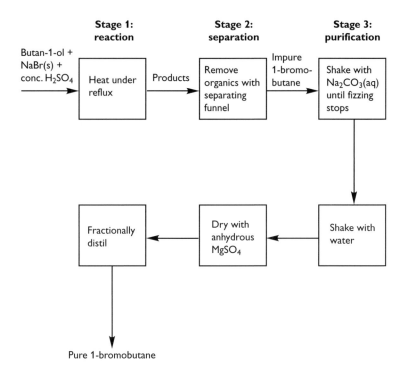

Stage 1: reaction — Butan-1-ol + NaBr(s) + conc. H_2SO_4 → Heat under reflux → Products

Stage 2: separation — Remove organics with separating funnel → Impure 1-bromo-butane

Stage 3: purification — Shake with $Na_2CO_3(aq)$ until fizzing stops → Shake with water → Dry with anhydrous $MgSO_4$ → Fractionally distil → Pure 1-bromobutane

Question 9

(a) Suggest some impurities in the mixture after Stage 2.

(b) Why is the organic layer shaken first with $Na_2CO_3(aq)$ and then with water?

(c) Suggest substances that are removed by distilling the dried bromobutane.

Reaction mechanisms

The best possible reaction mechanism for a chemist would be a sort of molecular 'movie'. It would be a record of everything that happens from when the reacting particles approach each other to when the product molecules are formed. Unfortunately, this amount of information is not available. However, we can make computer animations using information gained about crucial points (like single frames of a movie) in the progress of the reaction. These 'still images' are often all we have on which to base our 'reaction mechanism'.

In order to understand and write effective answers to questions on this topic, you need to be familiar with the concept of bond fission and the types of attacking reagent.

Bond fission means bond breaking. There are two ways in which a covalent bond can break. These are compared in the table below, using the C–Cl bond in chloromethane as an example.

	Homolytic fission (homolysis)	Heterolytic fission (heterolysis)
What happens to the bonding electon pair?	One electron goes to each atom $H-C-Cl$ (with H above and H below) ↓ $H-C\cdot + \cdot Cl$ (with H above and H below)	Both electrons go to the more electronegative atom $H-C-Cl$ (with H above and H below) ↓ $H-C^+ + :Cl^-$ (with H above and H below)
Species (atoms or group of atoms) formed	Radicals	Ions; if the resulting positive charge is on a carbon atom, the ion is called a **carbocation**
How does bond polarity favour the process?	Usually non-polar (e.g. C–H)	Usually polar (e.g. C–Cl)
Conditions favouring the process	Light (sometimes visible but usually ultraviolet); gas phase; non-polar solvents	Polar solvents

The species that attack carbon atoms in organic molecules are:

- **radicals** — atoms, molecules or ions that have at least one unpaired electron. **Biradicals** have two unpaired electrons. The most common example of a biradical is dioxygen (O_2). This is contrary to what dot-and-cross diagrams would have us believe! In the dot-and-cross diagram for dioxygen, all electrons are paired.

  This shows the limitations of such diagrams in helping us to explain the behaviour of every substance. Nevertheless, they are often very useful at A-level.
- **nucleophiles** — molecules or negative ions with a lone pair of electrons that can attack an electron-deficient carbon (positively charged) to form a covalent bond. Examples include H_2O, OH^- and NH_3.
- **electrophiles** — molecules or positive ions that can attack an electron-rich carbon (region of high electron density), accepting a pair of electrons to form a covalent bond. Examples include Br_2 and H^+.

Question 10

What do you call a molecule or negative ion that attacks an electron-deficient hydrogen atom?

Chain reactions

Chain reactions are extremely fast and often require visible or ultraviolet light (e.g. the reaction between chlorine and methane). They are known as **radical chain reactions**. A radical chain mechanism has three stages:

- **Initiation**: $Cl_2 \longrightarrow 2Cl\bullet$
- **Propagation**: $CH_4 + Cl\bullet \longrightarrow \bullet CH_3 + HCl$
$$\bullet CH_3 + Cl_2 \longrightarrow CH_3Cl + Cl\bullet$$
- **Termination**: $Cl\bullet + Cl\bullet \longrightarrow Cl_2$
$$\bullet CH_3 + Cl\bullet \longrightarrow CH_3Cl$$
$$\bullet CH_3 + \bullet CH_3 \longrightarrow C_2H_6$$

It is important to notice that the propagation step involves the chlorine radical ($Cl\bullet$) abstracting a hydrogen atom from a methane molecule, rather than attacking a carbon atom to form chloromethane and a hydrogen radical. Hydrogen abstraction reactions are common in the troposphere because radicals are plentiful.

Question 11

Why are replacements for CFCs designed to contain C–H bonds?

Types of reaction

Most organic reactions can be classified as redox, acid–base, **substitution**, **addition** or **elimination**. Substitution, addition and elimination reactions involve one of the three groups of attacking species — **radicals**, **electrophiles** or **nucleophiles**. The reaction of chloromethane with aqueous sodium hydroxide is an example of nucleophilic substitution.

Tip When asked to name the mechanism for a given reaction, you need to choose one word from each of the two categories given in bold above.

The mechanisms of the reactions covered at AS are summarised in the table below.

Type	Organic reactant	Reagent	Type of attacking species	Organic product
Substitution	Alkanes	Cl_2 with UV light	Radical	Halogenoalkanes
Substitution	Halogenoalkanes	H_2O^* or OH^-	Nucleophile	Alcohols
Substitution	Halogenoalkanes	NH_3	Nucleophile	Amines
Substitution	Alcohols	X^- (halide)	Nucleophile	Halogenoalkanes
Addition	Alkenes	Br_2	Electrophile	Dibromoalkanes
Addition	Alkenes	HBr	Electrophile	Bromoalkanes
Addition	Alkenes	H_2O	Electrophile	Alcohols
Elimination	Alcohols	H_2SO_4	None	Alkenes
*Nucleophilic substitution by water is also called hydrolysis.				

Question 12

Describe the difference between a hydrolysis reaction and a hydration reaction.

Describing mechanisms

Formulae, 'curly arrows' and a few words are all you need to fully describe a mechanism. You need to be able to describe the mechanisms for **nucleophilic substitution** and **electrophilic addition**. Remember, 'curly arrows' show the movement of electrons. An electron pair is indicated by a full arrow (⌒➤). A single electron is represented by a half-arrow (⌒).

Examples of nucleophilic substitution and electrophilic addition reactions are given below.

Bromoethane reacting with strong alkali

Bromine reacting with ethene

Carbocation
intermediate

Question 13

Using words rather than diagrams, describe the mechanisms for:
(a) nucleophilic substitution
(b) electrophilic addition
Which descriptive approach — labelled diagrams or written text — do you prefer?

Reactivity of halogenoalkanes

Which factor is more important in deciding the rate of hydrolysis of halogenoalkanes? Is it **bond polarity** or **bond strength**? If it is bond polarity, then iodo-compounds should react *more slowly* than chloro-compounds. However, C–I bonds are weaker than C–Cl bonds. Therefore, if bond strength is more important, iodo-compounds should react *faster* than chloro-compounds.

The **rate of hydrolysis** of halogenoalkanes is determined by reacting them with silver nitrate dissolved in aqueous ethanol. The purpose of the ethanol is to enable the halogenoalkane and aqueous solution to mix. The results for the reaction of various halogenobutanes with silver nitrate at 60°C are given in the table below.

	1-chlorobutane	1-bromobutane	1-iodobutane
Bond broken in reaction	C–Cl	C–Br	C–I
Electronegativity difference between halogen and carbon	0.6	0.4	0.1
Bond enthalpy/kJ mol^{-1}	346	290	228
Time for precipitate to appear	No precipitate after 30 minutes	About 15 minutes	About 2 minutes
Colour of precipitate	—	Cream	Yellow
Formula of precipitate	—	AgBr	AgI

These results indicate that the relative rates of reaction of halogenoalkanes depend on the *bond strength* of the carbon–halogen bond.

Tip Beware — in examinations, students often incorrectly choose the electronegativity factor in their explanations of halogenoalkane reactivity.

You should be able to write equations for the hydrolysis and precipitation reactions occurring. If you have difficulty with the precipitation reactions, refer to pages 22–23.

Question 14

Why does the rate of hydrolysis of halogenoalkanes depend on the strength of the carbon–halogen bond? Suggest a reason why chloroalkanes hydrolyse faster than fluoroalkanes.

Chlorofluorocarbons (CFCs)

You need to:
- know their uses
- understand their role in ozone depletion
- be able to explain why chemists thought they were safe
- be able to discuss the advantages and disadvantages of replacement compounds

CFCs contain C–F and C–Cl bonds, both of which are strong. Therefore, CFCs are unreactive in the troposphere. When CFCs eventually reach the stratosphere, ultraviolet radiation breaks the C–Cl bond homolytically.

Question 15

In a CFC molecule in the stratosphere, C–Cl rather than C–F bond breakage occurs. Explain why.

Use of CFCs

CFCs are used as:

- refrigerants in food refrigerators and air conditioning units
- propellants for aerosols
- blowing agents for making expanding plastics
- solvents for dry cleaning and for cleaning electronic circuitry

Advantages

- They are unreactive, non-toxic and non-flammable.
- They have the correct volatility for refrigerants — high enough to vaporise, but low enough to liquefy under pressure.
- They dissolve grease easily.

CFCs and some replacement compounds compared

The advantages and disadvantages of CFCs and some types of replacement compound are summarised in the following table. ODP stands for ozone depletion potential and is a measure of the ability of a compound to destroy ozone in the stratosphere. ODP is measured relative to CCl_3F (CFC-11), which is assigned a value of 1.0.

Group of compounds	Advantages	Disadvantages
CFCs	Listed above	High ODP (1.0) Cause greenhouse gases
HCFCs (hydrochlorofluorocarbons)	Low ODP (about 0.1)	Cause greenhouse gases More expensive Some are flammable
HFCs (hydrofluorocarbons)	ODP = 0	Cause greenhouse gases Much more expensive Some are flammable
Alkanes	ODP = 0 Cheap	Cause greenhouse gases Flammable Difficult to find compounds with the appropriate properties

Polymers

Poly(propene) is a polymer which has been designed. Many polymers have been discovered by accident. These include low-density poly(ethene), poly(tetrafluoroethene) (PTFE), conducting and light-emitting polymers, and bakelite.

Only **addition polymers** are studied at AS. Addition polymers are formed from alkene **monomers**. If two or more different monomers are polymerised together, the polymer is called a **copolymer**.

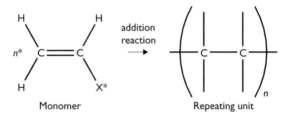

Monomer   Repeating unit

*n is a very large number and X is an H atom or a substituent group.

Common substituent groups are shown in the table below.

Alkene	Substituent group	Name of a polymer
$H_2C = C$ with H and Cl	Methyl	Poly(propene)
$H_2C = C$ with H and phenyl ring	Phenyl	Poly(phenylethene) or styrene
$H_2C = C$ with H and Cl	Chloro	Poly(chloroethene) or polyvinyl chloride (PVC)

Plastics contain other materials as well as the polymer. These may be pigments, lubricants, antioxidants or materials to increase the strength of the plastic, such as glass wool. Plastics can be moulded to a defined shape.

Plastics are either:
- **thermoplastics** (thermosoftening plastics). These contain polymers that soften on heating but become stiff and solid-like on cooling. This means that they can be remoulded. The polymer chains are able to move relative to each other.
- **thermosets** (thermosetting plastics). When these are first moulded, the heat causes

'crosslinks' to form between polymer chains. The resulting plastic is a covalently bonded network of atoms and is hard and rigid. On heating, bonds eventually break and the material 'chars' as carbon is formed.

Properties, structure and intermolecular forces

The properties of a polymer essentially depend on:

- how the polymer chains behave
- the strength and extent of the intermolecular forces between the polymer chains

First, consider the molecular structure of the polymer chains:

- Linear chains pack more closely than branched chains.
- Side groups oriented in a regular way pack closely together.
- Long side-chains become tangled.

Second, the properties of a polymer are affected by the strength and extent of the intermolecular forces between the chains. The most common intermolecular force affecting polymers such as poly(ethene) and poly(propene) is the instantaneous dipole–induced dipole.

- The longer the polymer chain, the more extensive are these forces.
- The more closely the polymer chains can come together, the greater the strength of these forces.

If the polymer has polar side-groups, then the stronger permanent dipole–permanent dipole forces (or even hydrogen bonding) are possible.

Crystalline polymers have areas in their structure where the chains are closely packed in a regular way. Areas where the chains are further apart are **amorphous**.

Flexibility in polymers requires the chains to be able to slide over one another. This happens because the intermolecular forces between the chains are weaker than those in a rigid polymer.

In general:

- the *more crystalline* a polymer, the *stronger* and *less flexible* it is
- the *longer* the chains in the polymer, the *stronger* it is

Questions using these ideas can be found on page 65.

Photochemistry

Prior knowledge

You are expected to know about:

- common gases in the atmosphere (GCSE)
- interaction of radiation with matter

Quantisation of energy

Quantisation of energy means that particles can only have certain fixed amounts of energy. When energy changes, it can only change by fixed amounts. Some important facts about the energy associated with electrons and molecules are summarised in the table below.

Energy	Spectrum corresponding to the spacing between the energy levels	Energy change caused by absorption of radiation/J
Electrons becoming excited	Visible and ultraviolet	1×10^{-19} to 1×10^{-16}
Bonds vibrating	Infrared	1×10^{-20} to 1×10^{-19}
Molecules rotating	Microwave	1×10^{-22} to 1×10^{-20}
Molecules translating (moving around)	The spacing is so tiny that translational energy is treated as continuous	

Question 16

Explain why it takes more energy for a C–F bond to vibrate than a C–Cl bond.

What can happen when molecules absorb ultraviolet radiation?

$h\nu$ is used to show the absorption of one photon of light (at AS we use the term 'light' to mean any form of radiation)

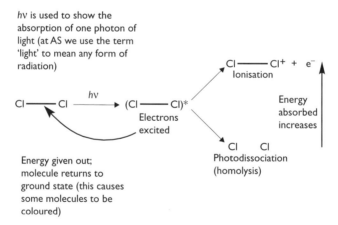

Energy given out; molecule returns to ground state (this causes some molecules to be coloured)

Ozone as a sunscreen

The formation and natural destruction of ozone occurs in the stratosphere. The formation of ozone takes place in two steps:

- Step 1 is called **photodissociation**.

    $O_2 + h\nu$ (ultraviolet) $\longrightarrow O + O$

- Step 2 is the reaction between oxygen atoms (produced by photodissociation) and oxygen molecules, to produce ozone.

    $O + O_2 \longrightarrow O_3$

The natural destruction of ozone is also a photodissociation reaction.

$$O_3 + h\nu \text{ (ultraviolet)} \longrightarrow O_2 + O$$

This last reaction is responsible for the screening effect of ozone.

Breaking a bond in ozone

You should be able to use the expression:

$$E = h\nu$$

to calculate the **frequency** needed to break a bond in an ozone molecule. You will be given its **bond enthalpy** and the **Planck constant** (h).

Example

The energy needed to break the O–O bonds in a mole of ozone is $392\,\text{kJ}\,\text{mol}^{-1}$.

The energy required to break one O–O bond is $\dfrac{392}{6.02 \times 10^{23}}$ kJ.

$$\text{frequency } (\nu) = \frac{E}{h}$$

where $h = 6.63 \times 10^{-34}\,\text{J}\,\text{Hz}^{-1}$.

$$\nu = \frac{392 \times 1000}{6.02 \times 10^{23}} \div 6.63 \times 10^{-34}\,\text{Hz}$$

$$= 9.82 \times 10^{14}\,\text{Hz}$$

Tip This is where attention to units pays dividends. Bond enthalpies are given in $\text{kJ}\,\text{mol}^{-1}$ but the units of h are $\text{J}\,\text{Hz}^{-1}$, hence the factor of 1000.

The greenhouse effect

A greenhouse gas is one that absorbs infrared radiation in the troposphere. Neither visible nor ultraviolet radiation is absorbed. Some common gases in the atmosphere that absorb infrared radiation are given in the table below.

Name	Formula	Concentration in the troposphere/ppm	Greenhouse factor*
Nitrogen	N_2	7.8×10^5	Negligible
Oxygen	O_2	2.1×10^5	Negligible
Argon	Ar	1.0×10^4	Negligible
Water vapour	H_2O	c. 1.0×10^4 (variable)	0.1
Carbon dioxide	CO_2	3.7×10^2	1
Methane	CH_4	1.8	20
CFC-11	CCl_3F	2.6×10^{-4}	3800
CFC-12	CCl_2F_2	5.3×10^{-4}	8100
*The greenhouse factor compares the greenhouse effect for a gas molecule with that of carbon dioxide, which is assigned a value of 1.			

Question 17

Using the data in the table, explain why carbon dioxide makes the largest contribution to the total greenhouse effect.

If you are asked to explain the greenhouse effect, base your answer on the following outline:

- Most radiation that reaches the troposphere is absorbed by the Earth.
- The Earth's surface warms up and *emits infrared radiation*.
- Some of this emitted infrared radiation is *absorbed* by greenhouse gases.
- The greenhouse gas molecules gain *vibrational* energy (or bonds in the molecules vibrate faster).
- The average *kinetic energy* of the gas in the troposphere increases, leading to an increase in the average *temperature* of the atmosphere.

Tip The words in italics are key words which an examiner will expect to see used correctly by good candidates.

Chemical equilibrium

Prior knowledge

You are expected to know about reversible reactions.

Dynamic equilibrium

The concept of chemical equilibrium applies to **closed systems** only. A closed system is one that cannot exchange mass with its surroundings. For a reaction in an open vessel to be a closed system, there must be no gaseous reactants or products. If gases are present, the vessel must have a lid for chemical equilibrium to be achieved.

Chemical equilibrium involves **dynamic** processes. Nothing *appears* to be changing. However, reactant particles are colliding and forming product particles and product particles are also colliding, forming reactant particles. At equilibrium, the rates of these two processes are equal.

Using Le Chatelier's principle

Le Chatelier's principle states that, *for a system in equilibrium*, when a change is made in any of the conditions, the equilibrium position will move in the direction that counteracts the change.

The effects of changing conditions on the equilibrium position of some reactions are summarised in the table.

Condition change	Effect on equilibrium position
Increasing the concentration of reactants	Moves to the right
Increasing the concentration of products	Moves to the left
Decreasing the concentration of reactants	Moves to the left
Decreasing the concentration of products	Moves to the right
Increasing the pressure for a reaction in which the products have fewer gas molecules than the reactants	Moves to the right
Decreasing the pressure for a reaction in which the products have fewer gas molecules than the reactants	Moves to the left
Increasing the temperature for a reaction in which the forward reaction is exothermic	Moves to the left
Increasing the temperature for a reaction in which the forward reaction is endothermic	Moves to the right

The presence of a **catalyst** does *not* affect the equilibrium position. It speeds up the forward and backward reactions to the same extent.

Carbon dioxide in the atmosphere and the oceans

The atmosphere and the oceans are treated as a closed system. Gaseous carbon dioxide dissolves in water and reacts to form a weakly acidic solution. You should be able to write the equations for the equilibria occurring:

$$CO_2(g) \rightleftharpoons CO_2(aq)$$
$$CO_2(aq) + H_2O(l) \rightleftharpoons HCO_3^-(aq) + H^+(aq)$$

Question 18

The solubility of CO_2 is greater at the bottom of the ocean than near the surface. Use Le Chatelier's principle to explain this.

Rate of reaction

Prior knowledge

You are expected to know about:
- factors affecting the rate of a reaction (GCSE)
- simple collision theory (GCSE)
- heterogeneous catalysis
- enthalpy changes

Factors affecting reaction rates

In order to react, particles must collide. The number, frequency and energy of collisions affect reaction rate. This is called **collision theory**.

Concentration of reactants

Remember that, for gases, concentration is proportional to pressure.

The effect of concentration on reaction rate can be explained using collision theory:
- Reacting particles collide.
- Collisions having the minimum kinetic energy (the activation enthalpy) lead to products.
- An increase in concentration/pressure increases the total number of collisions. The number of collisions leading to products also increases.

Temperature
- An increase in temperature increases the average kinetic energy of the particles.
- A greater number of collisions will have energy greater than the activation enthalpy.
- More collisions will be successful in forming products.

There is also a slight increase in the collision frequency with increasing temperature, but the main effect on reaction rate is from the increase in the average kinetic energy of the particles.

Presence of a catalyst
- A catalyst provides an alternative reaction pathway that has a *lower* activation enthalpy.
- A greater number of collisions will have energy greater than the activation enthalpy, so the rate is increased.

Particle size of a solid reactant or catalyst

A decrease in particle size means an increase in surface area. The number of collisions at the surface of the solid increases; therefore, the reaction rate increases.

Intensity of light or ultraviolet radiation in photochemical reactions

An increase in the intensity of light or ultraviolet radiation increases the number of bonds broken, forming more radicals. Therefore, the reaction rate increases.

Catalysts

There are two types of catalyst, heterogeneous and homogeneous. These are compared in the table below.

	Heterogeneous	Homogeneous
Phase	Different (e.g. gaseous reactants and a solid catalyst)	Same (e.g. reactants and catalyst both in solution or both in gas phase)
Examples	• Hydrogenation of alkenes with a platinum or nickel catalyst • Manufacture of ethanol from steam and ethene using phosphoric acid on a silica support	• Chlorine radicals in the depletion of stratospheric ozone • Enzymes
How does the catalyst work?	• Reactants are adsorbed onto the surface of the catalyst and bonds are weakened • Bonds break • New bonds form • Products desorb from the surface and diffuse away	• Usually one reactant forms an intermediate with the catalyst • The intermediate reacts further to form the products and regenerate the catalyst

Tip At AS, 'phase' is taken to mean the same as 'state'.

Answers to questions

Question 1

The *f*-orbitals first occur in the fourth period.

Question 2

(a) • Metallic elements have atoms.

   • Non-metallic elements form molecules (noble gases are single atoms) or networks.

   • Compounds formed between metals and non-metals have ionic bonding, and therefore ions are present.

   • Compounds between non-metals have covalent bonding and are molecular or networks.

   • Acidic or alkaline solutions, formed by adding water to some molecular compounds, contain ions.

(b) • KBr: ions

   • SF_6: molecules

   • Cu: atoms

   • Poly(butene): molecules

   • HBr(aq): ions

Question 3

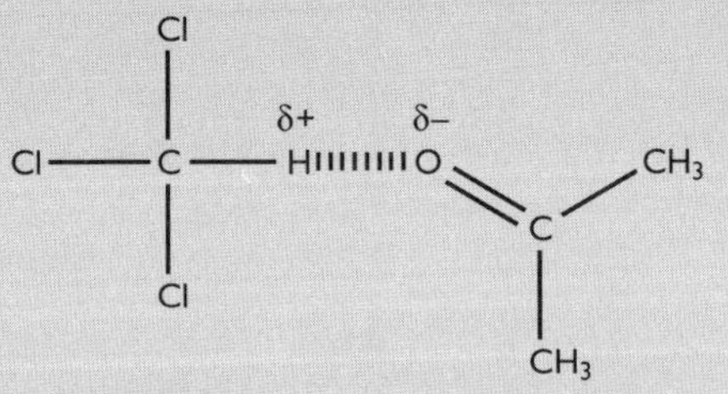

Question 4

Sulphur in $Na_2S_2O_3$: +2
Nitrogen in NO_3^-: +5
Phosphorus in P_2O_3: +3
Nitrogen in NH_4^+: −3

Question 5

Either of the following:
$H_2O + Cl^- \rightleftharpoons OH^- + HCl$
$H_3O^+ + Cl^- \rightleftharpoons H_2O + HCl$

Question 6

Chloride ions have three electron shells (2, 8, 8); sodium ions have two electron shells (2, 8).

Question 7

(a) The colourless solution turns yellow.

(b) $2I^-(aq) + Cl_2(aq) \longrightarrow 2Cl^-(aq) + I_2(aq)$

Question 8
The ring prevents the single C–C bond between the two Br atoms from rotating:

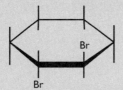 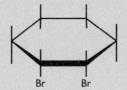

Question 9
(a) Butan-1-ol, acid, water, butenes (due to elimination reactions)
(b) With Na_2CO_3 to remove any acid; with water to remove any Na_2CO_3
(c) Butan-1-ol, butenes

Question 10
Base, because the OH⁻ is acting as a proton acceptor. OH⁻ is a better nucleophile than a base in reactions with halogenoalkanes.

Question 11
There is a plentiful supply of radicals in the troposphere that can abstract a hydrogen atom from C–H. Molecules containing Cl and F are broken down, so fail to reach the stratosphere.

Question 12
In hydrolysis, water breaks down a substance forming at least two products. In hydration, water adds to a compound, forming a single substance.

Question 13
(a) In nucleophilic substitution, a hydroxide ion donates a pair of electrons to the electron-deficient carbon bonded to the bromine atom. A covalent bond is formed and at the same time the C–Br bond breaks heterolytically to form a bromide ion and an alcohol.
(b) In electrophilic addition, as the bromine molecule approaches ethene, the high electron density of the C=C bond polarises it, with the nearer bromine atom becoming slightly positively charged. This electrophilic bromine accepts an electron pair from the C=C bond, forming a C–Br covalent bond. At the same time, the Br–Br bond breaks heterolytically, forming a bromide ion and a carbocation intermediate. The bromide ion is attracted to the carbocation and a covalent bond is formed.

Question 14
To break the carbon–halogen bond, the activation enthalpy for the hydrolysis of halogenoalkanes must be exceeded. A C–F bond is much stronger than a C–Cl bond. Chloroalkanes are therefore more easily hydrolysed.

Question 15
A C–F bond is much stronger than a C–Cl bond. A C–Cl bond requires radiation of a lower frequency than a C–F bond to break it.

Question 16

A C–F bond is stronger than a C–Cl bond. It needs more energy to stretch it and to cause it to vibrate. A higher infrared frequency is needed, since $E = h\nu$.

Question 17

Although methane and CFCs have higher greenhouse factors than CO_2, the concentration of CO_2 is much higher than those of methane and CFCs. Therefore, its overall effect on global warming is more significant.

Question 18

At the bottom of the ocean, the pressure is greater. This increased pressure causes the equilibrium position for the dissolution of gaseous CO_2 molecules in water to move to the right. More gaseous CO_2 will dissolve.

Questions
&
Answers

This section contains questions similar in style to those in the Unit 2 test. The questions begin with a sentence or two to set the context for the structured parts that follow. This context is called the **stem**.

At AS, some of the contexts of the questions are based on those in the course materials. Others may introduce chemical substances and applications not previously encountered. Either way, these are only vehicles to introduce questions based on the chemical knowledge and ideas laid out in the specification. The context can usually be classified under one of the three teaching sections of the unit and should give you an insight into which aspect of the course is being examined.

Papers are designed to be accessible to candidates who have gained a grade C in double award science at GCSE. Sometimes it is easy to miss the obvious, because only GCSE knowledge is required!

In this guide, there are four questions for each of the three unit sections:

Set 1: from minerals to elements
Question 1: bromine from the sea
Question 2: copper extraction
Question 3: photography
Question 4: zinc extraction

Set 2: the atmosphere
Question 1: sun screening and ozone depletion
Question 2: halogenoalkanes
Question 3: the greenhouse effect, global warming and the oceans
Question 4: catalytic hydrogenation

Set 3: the polymer revolution
Question 1: poly(ethene)
Question 2: polymers that dissolve in water
Question 3: polymers that conduct electricity
Question 4: alcohols in fuel oil

How to use this section
There are several ways of using these questions and answers. You could read about the appropriate context in your course materials and notes and then tackle the particular question, taking account of the advice given on pages 8–9. Where there is a mark available in extended writing questions for the quality of written communication, this is indicated by QWC. The answers given are model responses. Together with the examiner's comments, they should enable you to assess your own performance.

Examiner's comments
In the answers to questions with more than one marking point, each mark allocation is indicated by ✓. Where appropriate, the answers are followed by examiner's comments. These are preceded by the icon *e*. They point out where credit is due, specific problems and common errors.

Set 1

From minerals to elements

(1) In the UK, bromine is extracted from seawater. First, the seawater is treated with chlorine.

(a) (i) Write an ionic equation for the reaction of chlorine with bromide ions in seawater. Include state symbols in your equation. (3 marks)

(ii) What can you conclude about the relative reactivity of halogens from this reaction? Give a reason for your answer. (1 mark)

(b) The resulting bromine concentration in the water is very low, but is increased by further processing. The bromine is removed as vapour and treated with water and sulphur dioxide. The reaction is:

$$Br_2 + SO_2 + H_2O \longrightarrow HBr + H_2SO_4$$

(i) Balance the equation. (1 mark)

(ii) Give the oxidation states of:

- Br in Br_2
- S in SO_2
- Br in HBr
- S in H_2SO_4 (4 marks)

(iii) Give the formula of the reducing agent in this reaction. Explain your answer. (2 marks)

(c) In the final stage, bromine is regenerated using a redox reaction. Suggest a suitable reagent for treating the HBr. (1 mark)

(d) A sample of seawater contains 8.75×10^{-4} mol dm^{-3} of bromide ion (A_r: Br, 79.9). Calculate the maximum mass of bromine that could be produced from 1000 dm^3 of seawater. (3 marks)

Total: 15 marks

Answer to Question 1

(a) (i) $2Br^-(aq) + Cl_2(aq) \longrightarrow 2Cl^-(aq) + Br_2(aq)$ ✓✓✓

There are usually 3 marks for ionic equations: 1 mark for the correct formulae, 1 mark for the balance and 1 mark for the state symbols. In this case, $Cl_2(g)$ and $Br_2(g)$ would also be acceptable.

(ii) Chlorine is more reactive than bromine because it displaces bromine from a solution of bromide ions ✓.

There is only 1 mark for this question despite two apparent marking points. The first point is a 50:50 choice — these are not given credit by exam boards. The correct reason gains the mark. 'Oxidises', rather than 'displaces', would also be correct.

(b) (i) $Br_2 + SO_2 + \mathbf{2}H_2O \longrightarrow \mathbf{2}HBr + H_2SO_4$ ✓

You would also gain the mark for

$$2Br_2 + 2SO_2 + 4H_2O \longrightarrow 4HBr + 2H_2SO_4$$

(ii) Br in Br_2: 0 ✓
S in SO_2: +4 ✓
Br in HBr: −1 ✓
S in H_2SO_4: +6 ✓

There is 1 mark for each oxidation state, complete with sign. Remember to give positive signs as well as negative ones. Leaving out the positive signs would lose 2 marks here.

(iii) SO_2 ✓ because it loses electrons ✓

'Because Br_2 gains electrons' would also be acceptable. Answers in terms of oxidation state changes would also be correct, for example 'SO_2 ✓ because its oxidation state increases ✓'.

(c) Chlorine ✓

For industrial processes, always choose the obvious and cheapest chemical. In this case they already use chlorine in the first part of the process.

(d) moles of bromide ion in $1000\,dm^3$ of seawater = $8.75 \times 10^{-4} \times 1000$ mol ✓
mass of Br = $8.75 \times 10^{-4} \times 1000 \times 79.9$ g ✓
= 69.9 g ✓

In this calculation, the second mark is for moles multiplied by 79.9, irrespective of whether the value for moles is correct or not. You are not asked for a particular number of significant figures, so you should go for three.

■ ■ ■

(2) Most copper ores contain metal sulphides. Chalcocite has the formula Cu_2S. Copper ores rarely contain more than 1% copper. To obtain copper metal, the copper ore has to be concentrated, smelted and purified.

(a) Suggest *one* method by which grains of copper mineral can be separated from the crushed ore. (1 mark)

(b) Smelting involves roasting chalcocite in air. Sulphur dioxide is also formed. Write a balanced equation for the reaction that takes place during smelting. (2 marks)

(c) Describe and explain *two* environmental implications of the concentrating and smelting processes. (4 marks)

(d) Copper and sulphur are in different blocks in the periodic table.

(i) State which blocks copper and sulphur are in. (2 marks)

(ii) The atomic (proton) number of sulphur is 16. Complete the boxes below showing the electron configuration of sulphur atoms. (2 marks)

(iii) Explain your choice of answer for sulphur in (i). (1 mark)

(e) The large amounts of sulphur dioxide formed in smelting are converted to sulphuric acid. Pure sulphuric acid forms ions in water. The first step in the process is shown in the equation below.

$$H_2SO_4 + H_2O \longrightarrow H_3O^+ + HSO_4^-$$

In this reaction, water is acting as a base.

(i) Describe how water acts as a base. (2 marks)

(ii) Give the formula of the acid formed when water acts as a base. (1 mark)

Total: 15 marks

Answer to Question 2

(a) Froth flotation ✓

(b) $Cu_2S + O_2 \rightleftharpoons 2Cu + SO_2$ ✓✓

Remember that CuO is not formed. There is a clue in the stem of the question when it mentions smelting. There is 1 mark for the correct formulae and 1 mark for balancing.

(c) There will be a massive amount of waste rock from concentrating ✓. This will be an eyesore ✓. SO_2 is emitted during smelting ✓. It is a pollutant and a cause of acid rain ✓.

Remember that you need to make four points, two of which are explanations of the two problems identified. You could have 'wasteful of energy' instead of 'eyesore', but not 'expensive', since cost is not an environmental issue. 'Pollutant' is too vague for a mark by itself; you need to identify the effect. 'Causes photochemical smog' or 'harmful because it causes respiratory illness' would also gain a mark.

(d) (i) Cu is in the *d*-block ✓; S is in the *p*-block ✓.

(ii)

1s	2s	2p			3s	3p		
↓↑	↓↑	↓↑	↓↑	↓↑	↓↑	↓↑	↓	↓	✓✓

There is always 1 easy mark for adding the correct number of electrons, in this case 14 more. Remember to check your periodic table! The second mark is for the correct arrangement.

(iii) In sulphur, *p*-orbitals are being filled ✓.

(e) (i) Water gains ✓ a proton ✓.

Hydrogen *ion* is acceptable for the second mark, but not hydrogen by itself.

(ii) H_3O^+ ✓

⌿ Choose the substance from the products side of the equation that has gained an H⁺ ion.

▪ ▪ ▪

(3) Silver salts are used in some forms of photography because they darken on exposure to light. The equation for the effect of light on silver chloride is:

$$2AgCl \longrightarrow 2Ag + Cl_2$$

(a) (i) State why the silver chloride crystals darken.   (1 mark)

   (ii) Name the type of reaction occurring.   (1 mark)

(b) The most common silver salt is silver nitrate. Solid silver chloride can be
    made by mixing aqueous solutions of silver nitrate and sodium chloride.

   (i) Silver nitrate solution is colourless. Describe the appearance of solid
        silver choride.   (1 mark)

   (ii) Write an ionic equation for this reaction. Include state symbols in your
        equation.   (3 marks)

   (iii) The silver nitrate solution contains hydrated silver ions. Draw a
        diagram to show how a water molecule interacts with a silver ion.   (2 marks)

(c) The reaction between silver nitrate and sodium chloride in solution is used
    to find how much chloride ion is present in seawater.
    On titration, a 25.00 cm^3 sample of seawater needed exactly 15.00 cm^3 of
    0.900 mol dm^{-3} silver nitrate solution. (1 mol of chloride ion reacts with
    1 mol of silver nitrate.)

   (i) Name the piece of apparatus used for adding silver nitrate solution in
        the titration.   (1 mark)

   (ii) Calculate the number of moles of silver nitrate reacting with the
        seawater sample.   (2 marks)

   (iii) Write down the number of moles of chloride ion in the seawater sample.   (1 mark)

   (iv) Calculate the concentration of chloride ions in seawater. Give your
        answer to three significant figures.   (3 marks)

Total: 15 marks

Answer to Question 3

(a) (i) Black particles of silver are formed ✓.

   (ii) Redox ✓

'Reduction' or 'oxidation' on its own will not score.

(b) (i) White ✓

You are asked for the *appearance* of a precipitate. For 1 mark there is no need to
describe particle size — just focus on colour.

(ii) $Ag^+(aq) + Cl^-(aq) \longrightarrow AgCl(s)$ ✓✓✓

There is 1 mark for the correct formula of the silver ion, 1 mark for the rest of the
equation being correct and 1 mark for state symbols. A common error is to write Ag^{2+}.
If you did this, but balanced the equation correctly for a 2+ charge, you would score
2 out of 3 marks.

(iii)

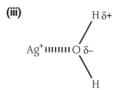

📝 There is 1 mark for a positively charged silver ion next to the oxygen atom of water and 1 mark for the correct partial charges on the OH bond. It is acceptable just to show the charge on one hydrogen atom.

(c) (i) Burette ✓

(ii) moles of silver nitrate added = $0.900 \times \dfrac{15.00}{1000}$ mol ✓

$$= 0.0135 \, \text{mol} \checkmark$$

📝 The first mark is awarded for having moles = concentration × volume.

(iii) moles of chloride ion in sample = 0.0135 mol ✓

(iv) concentration of chloride ions = $\dfrac{0.0135}{25.00/1000}$ ✓

$$= 0.540 \, \text{mol} \, \text{dm}^{-3} \checkmark$$

The third mark is awarded for giving the answer to three significant figures. The space for the answer on the exam paper would show the units for concentration ($\text{mol} \, \text{dm}^{-3}$).

■ ■ ■

(4) This question is designed to give you some practice with the statements in the specification about extracting pure metals from their ores and in the interpretation of flow diagrams.

The flow diagram below shows one method of extracting zinc and lead metals from a concentrated ore sample.

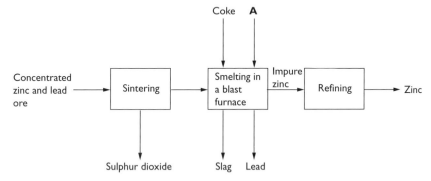

The ore contains mainly zinc minerals, with some lead and a small amount of other metals. The formulae of some of these minerals are given in the table.

Name of mineral	Formula
Zinc-blende	ZnS
Calamine	$ZnCO_3$
Galena	PbS

(a) The ore has been concentrated so that its metal content is at least 50%. It is made into a sinter, which is a hard, porous solid. The sinter is formed by heating the ore containing the minerals in air, where they burn, leaving the metals present as their oxides. Gases are given off from the solid mass leaving the sinter. Some of the gas is then converted into sulphuric acid.

   (i) Use the table and other information given to identify two gases that are given off in the sintering process. (2 marks)

   (ii) Write a balanced equation for the conversion of calamine into zinc oxide. (2 marks)

   (iii) Suggest a reason why some of the gas is converted into sulphuric acid. (1 mark)

   (iv) Suggest a reason why the ore is sintered before it is smelted. (1 mark)

(b) The ore contains a great deal of rocky material, mainly consisting of silicon(IV) oxide, but with some limestone.

   (i) Using a diagram, describe the structure of silicon(IV) oxide. (2 marks)

   (ii) What name is given to this type of structure? (1 mark)

(c) Zinc is smelted in a blast furnace in a manner similar to iron. The boiling point of zinc is 903°C. Lead melts at 228°C and boils at 1740°C. The temperature of the blast furnace is kept above 1000°C.

   (i) Name substance A, shown in the flow diagram. (1 mark)

   (ii) Write a balanced equation for the reduction of zinc oxide, ZnO, by carbon monoxide. Give state symbols in your equation. (2 marks)

   (iii) Explain how zinc and lead are separated from each other in the furnace. (2 marks)

   (iv) Suggest what happens to the silicon(IV) oxide and limestone from the ore concentrate. (1 mark)

Total: 15 marks

Answer to Question 4

(a) (i) Carbon dioxide ✓ and sulphur dioxide ✓

You should know that carbonates of group 2 and of transition metals decompose on heating, forming the metal oxide and carbon dioxide. Formulae would be acceptable answers, since you are asked only to *identify* (not *name*) the gases.

(ii) $ZnCO_3$ ✓ $\rightleftharpoons$ $ZnO + CO_2$ ✓

There is 1 mark for the correct left-hand side of the equation and 1 mark for the correct right-hand side.

(iii) A lot of sulphur dioxide is produced. A profit can be made by using it to make sulphuric acid ✓.

📖 The following is also a valid answer: 'Sulphur dioxide is a pollutant (producing acid rain or smog, which causes respiratory illness). Its emission into the atmosphere is strictly controlled by law.' In this type of question, where a reason for using a particular reaction, process or technique is asked for, the answer invariably involves cost, environmental or safety issues.

(iv) To produce a material with a large surface area so that smelting is more efficient ✓.

Other acceptable answers include:
- to turn the minerals into oxides
- to get rid of the sulphur
- to make it porous so that reacting and product gases can move through the packed furnace
- increase its strength and thus prevent the lumps being crushed in the process

(b) (i)

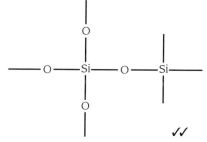

There is 1 mark for showing a silicon atom bonded to four oxygen atoms and 1 mark for showing oxygen bonded to two silicon atoms. There is no need to attempt an impossible three-dimensional structure — you have not been asked for this in the question.

(ii) Network ✓

Giant is also correct.

(c) (i) Air ✓

Oxygen is acceptable at AS, but you should really recognise that it is air that is used in the blast furnace.

(ii) $ZnO(s) + CO(g) \rightleftharpoons Zn(g) + CO_2(g)$ ✓✓

There is 1 mark for a correct balanced equation and 1 mark for the correct state symbols. Using the data given in the question you should be able to deduce that zinc is present as a vapour.

(iii) Zinc distils off as a vapour ✓, molten lead is tapped off at the bottom as a liquid ✓.

Use the temperature data given in the question; the boiling point of zinc is lower than the temperature of the furnace, whereas the boiling point of lead is higher. Stating that lead was left in the furnace would also gain the second mark.

(iv) They form slag ✓.

More detailed answers might state that limestone decomposes to calcium oxide which combines with the silicon(IV) oxide to form calcium silicate.

Set 2

The atmosphere

(1) Although there is only a small amount of ozone in the stratosphere (upper atmosphere), it is a vital sunscreen. Ozone is formed when oxygen molecules and oxygen atoms combine.

(a) Both oxygen molecules and atoms are radicals. What does this tell you about their electron structures? *(1 mark)*

(b) Oxygen atoms are formed when oxygen molecules absorb ultraviolet radiation of the appropriate frequency.

    (i) The bond enthalpy of an O=O bond is +498 kJ mol⁻¹. Calculate the energy in J needed to break an O=O bond in a single molecule. (Avogadro constant = 6.02×10^{23} mol⁻¹) *(2 marks)*

    (ii) Use $E = h\nu$ to calculate the minimum frequency needed to break an O=O bond. ($h = 6.63 \times 10^{-34}$ J Hz⁻¹) *(2 marks)*

(c) Give two ways ozone molecules are destroyed *naturally* in the stratosphere. *(2 marks)*

(d) Until the latter part of the twentieth century, the rates of formation and destruction of ozone were the same. Therefore, the concentration of ozone in the stratosphere was constant. However, in recent years, CFCs have had a devastating effect on the ozone concentration, reducing it drastically in some places. CFC-13 has the formula $CClF_3$.

    (i) Give the systematic name for CFC-13. *(2 marks)*

    (ii) In the stratosphere, the C–Cl bond in CFC-13 can be broken homolytically. Write down the formulae for the two products formed in this process. *(2 marks)*

    (iii) Explain how CFCs cause ozone to be destroyed in the atmosphere. *(4 marks)*

Total: 15 marks

Answer to Question 1

(a) They have at least one unpaired ✓ electron.

    Spare or lone electron would also gain the mark, whereas free, unshared or single electron would not.

(b) (i) Energy of O=O bond = $\dfrac{+498 \times 10^3}{6.02 \times 10^{23}}$ J per bond ✓

                = 8.27×10^{-19} J ✓

    (ii) $\nu = \dfrac{8.27 \times 10^{-19}}{6.63 \times 10^{-34}}$ Hz ✓

          = 1.25×10^{15} Hz ✓

    Remember, the space for the answers on the exam paper would show the units for energy (J) in (i) and frequency (Hz) in (ii). However, many students forget to convert kJ into J, which would lose 1 of the 2 marks for (i). Try to remember that visible and ultraviolet frequencies are around 10^{14}–10^{15} Hz.

(c) By photodissociation ✓ and by reacting with oxygen atoms ✓

Absorption of ultraviolet light is an acceptable alternative for photodissociation. Reaction of ozone with OH or NO radicals (formed naturally in the atmosphere) would gain credit, but not reaction with Cl because this arises from the photodissociation of CFCs and other man-made, halogen-containing compounds. Answers in terms of the appropriate equations would also gain the marks.

(d) (i) Chlorotrifluoromethane ✓✓

There is **1** mark for either chlorotrifluoromethane or trifluorochloromethane. The second mark is for putting the halogens in the correct order.

(ii) CF_3 ✓ and Cl ✓

There is no need to show the unpaired electrons or the full structures unless they are asked for.

(iii) CFCs are broken down by ultraviolet light giving Cl atoms ✓, which react with ozone molecules to form ClO radicals ✓. These re-form Cl atoms ✓. Therefore, they act as catalysts, breaking down many ozone molecules ✓.

The first marking point would sometimes score 2 marks in other questions, but here the information given in the question allows only 1 mark. An alternative marking point is that ClO radicals react with oxygen atoms. Some of the points could be made using the appropriate equations.

■ ■ ■

(2) Chloroethane, C_2H_5Cl, is used as a local anaesthetic, particularly by dentists. It is a gas at room temperature and pressure, but is easily liquefied under pressure.
(a) Use the electronegativity data (C, 2.6; H, 2.2; Cl, 3.2) to deduce whether chloroethane is a polar molecule or not. Give your reasoning. (2 marks)
(b) Chloroethane can be made from ethane and chlorine.
  (i) Give the condition necessary for the reaction to occur at room temperature. (1 mark)
  (ii) The mechanism of the reaction is a radical chain reaction.
    Write equations for the initiation step and two propagation steps. (3 marks)
  (iii) A small amount of butane is formed during the reaction.
    Suggest a termination step to account for this. (1 mark)
(c) A chemist wants to see if bromoethane can be used as an anaesthetic. He decides to make a sample of bromoethane by reacting ethanol with concentrated hydrogen bromide. After separating the impure bromoethane layer from the reaction mixture and purifying it, he obtains a colourless liquid.
  (i) What piece of laboratory equipment is used to separate the impure bromoethane layer? (1 mark)
  (ii) The impure bromoethane is first treated with a 5% sodium hydrogencarbonate solution and then with distilled water. Explain the purpose of these two steps. (2 marks)

(iii) **After these steps, the liquid product is slightly cloudy. Suggest why the liquid is cloudy and state what is added to make the liquid clear.** (2 marks)

(iv) **The bromoethane is now almost pure. The liquid contains a small amount of ethanol. What method could be used to achieve pure bromoethane?** (1 mark)

(d) **In the reaction of ethanol with HBr, a bromide ion attacks a carbon atom.**

(i) **In this reaction, what type of reagent is the bromide ion?** (1 mark)

(ii) **Why does the bromide ion attack the carbon next to the oxygen in an ethanol molecule?** (1 mark)

Total: 15 marks

Answer to Question 2

(a) The C–Cl bond is polar because there is an appreciable electronegativity difference of 0.6 between chlorine (3.2) and carbon (2.6) ✓. Since there is only one C–Cl bond, the molecule is polar ✓.

There is 1 mark for using the data and 1 mark for deducing why the molecule is polar. Often there are more marks available in this type of question. You could be asked for the partial charges or you may have to consider the molecule's shape if there were more than one polar bond. Remember, C–H bonds are considered to be essentially non-polar, even though the electronegativity difference is 0.4.

(b) (i) Ultraviolet radiation ✓

Ultraviolet light is acceptable, but not light by itself.

(ii) Initiation: $Cl_2 \longrightarrow 2Cl$ ✓
Propagation: $C_2H_6 + Cl \longrightarrow C_2H_5 + HCl$ ✓
$C_2H_5 + Cl_2 \longrightarrow C_2H_5Cl + Cl$ ✓
(iii) $2C_2H_5 \longrightarrow C_4H_{10}$ ✓

This is a difficult question and requires a good knowledge of chain reactions to sort it out. In termination steps, two radicals combine together. Hence, two different radicals give rise to three possible termination reactions.

(c) (i) Separating funnel ✓
(ii) The sodium carbonate reacts with any traces of excess acid ✓. The water is to wash out traces of the sodium carbonate ✓.

Traces of soluble inorganic substances produced by the reaction of the sodium carbonate will also be present. These are also washed out by the water.

(iii) The liquid contains water ✓. Dry with anhydrous magnesium sulphate ✓.

Other drying agents, such as anhydrous calcium chloride or anhydrous copper(II) sulphate, can be used.

(iv) Fractional distillation ✓

Distillation by itself would gain the mark.

(d) (i) Nucleophile ✓
    (ii) It is the carbon atom with the highest partial positive charge ✓.

Alternatively, it is the most electron-deficient carbon atom. There is only **1** mark available, so there is no point discussing how the electronegative oxygen atom makes the carbon atom slightly positive.

■ ■ ■

(3) Even though the proportion of carbon dioxide in the atmosphere is fairly small, about **0.037%** at present, it has an important effect on the temperature of the troposphere (lower atmosphere). In 1960, the concentration of carbon dioxide was about **0.032%**. Scientists suggest that this increase is the main cause of global warming.

  (a) Explain, using chemical ideas, how an increase in the concentration of carbon dioxide in the troposphere leads to an increase in the temperature of the troposphere. *In this question, 1 mark is for QWC.*   (6 marks)

  (b) Calculations based on how much carbon dioxide is being emitted suggest that the increase in the proportion of carbon dioxide should be about twice what it is. However, large amounts of this carbon dioxide dissolve in the oceans.

    (i) Describe *one* cause of the increasing concentration of carbon dioxide in the atmosphere.   (1 mark)

    (ii) The carbon dioxide in the atmosphere is in equilibrium with carbon dioxide in the ocean surface-water. Some of this carbon dioxide reacts with the water:

$$CO_2(g) \rightleftharpoons CO_2(aq) \qquad\qquad\qquad \text{equation 1}$$
$$CO_2(aq) + H_2O(l) \rightleftharpoons HCO_3^-(aq) + H^+(aq) \qquad \text{equation 2}$$

    Use equations 1 and 2 and Le Chatelier's principle to explain how the oceans reduce the concentration of carbon dioxide in the atmosphere.   (5 marks)

    (iii) What other information do you need to know about the reaction described by equation 2 in order to predict the effect of temperature on the acidity of the water? Explain your reasoning.   (3 marks)

                                  Total: 15 marks

Answer to Question 3

(a) The Earth *emits* ✓ infrared radiation ✓ which is *absorbed* ✓ by carbon dioxide molecules in the atmosphere. This radiation causes the molecules to *vibrate* ✓ *faster* ✓. Therefore, the average kinetic energy of the molecules in the atmosphere increases and the temperature rises ✓.

🖉 There are only 5 marks allocated for content, but six marking points are identified. This is often the case in extended writing answers. It is usually possible to convey a full understanding without making every point. To gain the QWC mark, there must be at least two sentences or bullet points that use *two* of the words in italics correctly. The 'faster' mark could also be gained by writing 'causes an increase in (kinetic) energy'. The last marking point is for linking an increase in energy to an increase in temperature.

Many students gain few or no marks on this type of question. First, they fail to focus on the Earth and start writing about emission of ultraviolet radiation by the sun, which often does wonderful things to greenhouse gases! The space for the answer is filled and nothing relevant has been written. Second, there is a tendency for students to rely on their 'general knowledge' for this type of topic. Unfortunately, this may have been culled from popular texts and papers and involve phrases such as 'reflects like a mirror', 'bounces off' or 'acts as a blanket'. Use chemical terminology and ideas logically and get the processes involved clear in your own mind. It is not possible to learn such topics parrot fashion. 6 marks out of 90 can be significant!

(b) (i) Increased use of fossil fuels ✓

Deforestation is also valid. There is no need to give details about the type and use of a particular fuel, or details about photosynthesis.

(ii) An increase in the concentration ✓ of CO_2 in the atmosphere will cause ✓ the equilibrium position of equation 1 to move to the right ✓, increasing the concentration of CO_2 in the oceans. This will cause ✓ the equilibrium position in equation 2 to move to the right ✓, therefore lowering the proportion of CO_2 in the air ✓.

There are six scoring points here, but only 5 marks to be gained. You *must* have the first point about concentration of CO_2 for the first mark because this concept is fundamental to the understanding of chemical equilibria and the use of Le Chatelier's principle. Then, any four points from the remaining five would score. Remember to use the numbers for the equations — it saves much description. Do *not* restate the equations as the basis of your answer. Many students do this and fail to gain any credit. This is always one of the worst-tackled concepts in examinations at this level. Be careful!

(iii) Whether the reaction is exothermic or endothermic ✓. If the reaction was exothermic, an increase in temperature would move the equilibrium position to the left ✓. Therefore, the hydrogen ion concentration would decrease, lowering the acidity ✓.

The first mark could also be gained by 'the enthalpy change for the reaction'. For the second mark, Le Chatelier's principle is applied. Do *not* waste space and time quoting the principle — just show that you know how to use it. The final mark is for connecting acidity to the hydrogen ion *concentration*.

■ ■ ■

(4) The hydrogenation of alkenes is an important reaction in the manufacture of low-fat spreads. Chemists have made homogeneous catalysts that can be used instead of metals, which require higher temperatures.
   (a) (i) What does the word *homogeneous* say about the catalyst? (1 mark)
   (ii) Draw a labelled enthalpy profile diagram to show how a catalyst speeds up a chemical reaction. (5 marks)

(b) **An unsaturated compound, A, is catalytically hydrogenated using nickel. 1 mol of hydrogen reacts with 1 mol of compound A to form 1 mol of a saturated compound, B. The molecular formula of B is C_4H_{10}. A has two geometric isomers.**

(i) **Draw structural formulae for the two geometric isomers of A.** (2 marks)

(ii) **Name compound A.** (1 mark)

(c) **Nickel requires a temperature of 150°C to be effective as a catalyst. Explain, using collision theory, why the reaction requires a temperature of 150°C to proceed at a reasonable rate.** *In this question, 1 mark is for QWC.* (6 marks)

Total: 15 marks

Answer to Question 4

(a) (i) It is in the same phase as the reactants ✓.

'In the same state' is also acceptable.

(ii)

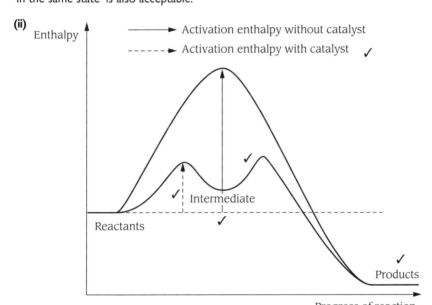

Questions asking you to complete an enthalpy diagram are often set. This question is harder because you have to remember what an enthalpy diagram is and then label your own drawing. There is 1 mark for labelling an activation enthalpy correctly. Double-headed arrows are acceptable at AS, but not at A2. There is 1 mark for the activation enthalpy of the catalysed reaction being lower than that of the uncatalysed reaction, and 1 mark for two 'humps' on the profile for the reaction in the presence of a catalyst. The final 2 marks are from three marking points:

• correct labels for the axes
• labelling reactants and products correctly
• labelling the 'trough' as intermediate

Remember, you have not been asked to describe the diagram in words or to explain how a catalyst works. Without a diagram, there would be no marks awarded.

(b) (i)

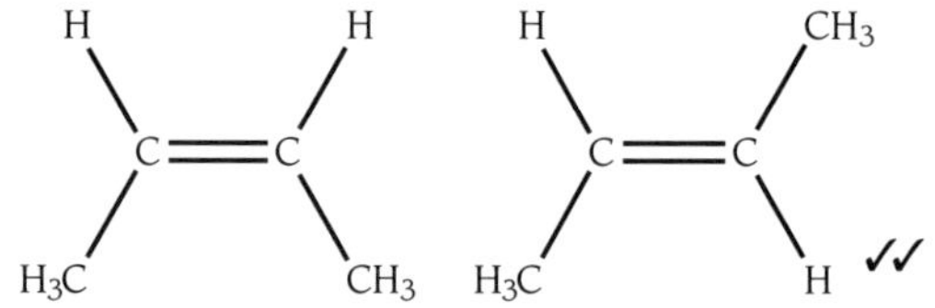

$$H_3C-CH=CH-CH_3 \quad \text{(cis and trans structures)} \checkmark\checkmark$$

It must be clear from the structures that one is the *cis* isomer and the other the *trans* isomer. There is no need to label them as such.

(ii) But-2-ene ✓

(c) For particles to react, they must collide ✓. For product molecules to form, the collision must have sufficient energy ✓. This energy is called the activation enthalpy for the reaction ✓. *At higher temperatures, the average kinetic energy of the particles is greater* ✓. Therefore, more collisions will have the necessary activation enthalpy ✓ and more product molecules will form, increasing the rate of reaction ✓.

🖉 There are six marking points but just 5 marks available. There is 1 mark for the marking point given in italics. Then any four from the remaining five points will score 1 mark each. Remember, it is both particles that collide that must have sufficient energy, not just one of them. Students often miss the last marking point, relying on examiners to infer that this is what they meant to say! The QWC mark requires the correct use of two of the following ideas and concepts:
● collisions between particles
● activation enthalpy (or energy)
● (kinetic) energy of particles

Set 3

The polymer revolution

(1) Low-density poly(ethene) (ldpe) was discovered by accident. That is, an experiment gave unexpected results. In this case, chemists were trying to use ethene and compound **A** to make compound **B**, using an addition reaction. The structure of compound **B** is:

Compound **B** C_2H_5

(a) (i) Name another polymer that was discovered by accident.   (1 mark)

(ii) Draw the full structural formula of ethene.   (1 mark)

(iii) Name the functional group attached to the benzene ring in compound **B**.   (1 mark)

(iv) Give the *molecular* formula of compound **A**.   (1 mark)

(b) Ldpe is an example of a thermoplastic polymer.

(i) Name the type of intermolecular force present in ldpe.   (1 mark)

(ii) Describe and explain what happens when a plastic article made from ldpe is heated and then cooled. *In this question, 1 mark is for QWC.*   (5 marks)

(c) Using Ziegler–Natta catalysts, chemists are able to make a higher-density form of poly(ethene), hdpe. Hdpe is more crystalline than ldpe. Suggest *two* ways in which the polymer chains in hdpe differ from those in ldpe.   (2 marks)

(d) Using these catalysts, propene, C_3H_8, can also be polymerised. Draw a diagram to show the structure of the repeating unit of poly(propene).   (1 mark)

(e) Two different types of poly(propene) are formed in this polymerisation. The structures are shown below. Their properties are very different.

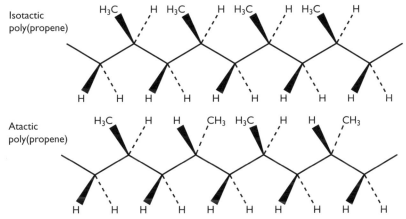

State which one is used as a weatherproof sealant. Describe and explain *one reason* for your choice.   (2 marks)

Total: 15 marks

Answer to Question 1

(a) (i) PTFE ✓

You do not need to write the name poly(tetrafluoroethene) for PTFE. Other possible answers are bakelite, light-emitting polymers or conducting polymers.

(ii)

$$\begin{array}{ccc} H & & H \\ \diagdown & & \diagup \\ & C = C & \\ \diagup & & \diagdown \\ H & & H \end{array}$$

Remember to show all bonds in a full structural formula. Always check the number of bonds.

(iii) Ketone ✓

Carbonyl is also an acceptable answer.

(iv) C_7H_6O ✓

At first sight, this question looks very hard. However, note the two important words: 'addition' and 'ethene'. You should then recognise that you need to take C_2H_4 away from the formula for compound B.

(b) (i) Instantaneous dipole–induced dipole ✓

A common mistake in naming intermolecular forces is to forget the second part, which indicates that it is an interaction. Many answers state simply instantaneous dipole or temporary dipole, which is not sufficient to gain the mark.

(ii) On heating, the plastic begins to soften and deform ✓. The intermolecular forces between the chains are broken by warming ✓ and the chains can move over each other ✓. On cooling, the plastic will have a different shape because the intermolecular forces will occur between different atoms ✓.

The first point can only be given for 'soften' if a changed or deformed shape is referred to on cooling. The QWC mark is awarded for using two of the following terms correctly, in two sentences or bullet points: intermolecular force; chains; deform.

(c) Closer together in hdpe ✓; less branched in hdpe ✓

This is a comparison, so you must make clear whether you are referring to hdpe or ldpe.

(d)

$$\left(\begin{array}{cc} H & CH_3 \\ | & | \\ -C - C- \\ | & | \\ H & H \end{array}\right)$$

The brackets are not essential, but the bonds linking the unit to further units are.

(e) The atactic polymer, because it is soft ✓ and flexible. Its structure makes it much less crystalline ✓ than the isotactic polymer.

Another word for 'much less crystalline' is amorphous. There are only 2 marks available, so there is no need to discuss intermolecular forces and how chains slide over one another. The question is trying to get you to focus on structural factors rather than intermolecular forces. Alternatively, the second mark can be scored for linking flexibility to the more irregular chain structure of the atactic polymer.

■ ■ ■

(2) Poly(ethenol) cannot be made by polymerising the monomer, because ethenol does not exist. Instead, it can be made from compound A in two stages.

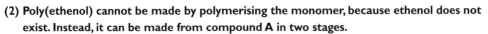

Compound **A**

Some polymers dissolve in water. These are forms of a polymer called poly(ethenol).

(a) Draw a skeletal formula for poly(ethenol), showing *three* monomer units. (2 marks)

(b) Compound A is an ester because it contains the ethanoate group.
  Draw the full structural formula for the ethanoate group. (1 mark)

The polymer made from compound **A** is insoluble in water. Its ester groups can be replaced with **OH** groups. Pure poly(ethenol) is actually insoluble in water, but as the percentage of **OH** groups decreases, the resulting polymer becomes soluble. However, if the percentage of **OH** groups decreases too much, the polymer again becomes insoluble.

(c) What name is given to the *type* of reaction in which compound A is
  polymerised? (1 mark)

(d) (i) Draw the structural formulae of *two* water molecules, showing how
  they can form a hydrogen bond. Indicate clearly any partial charges. (3 marks)

  (ii) Explain, in terms of intermolecular forces, why the solubility in water
  of the polymer varies with the percentages of ester and OH groups.
  Comment on whether polymers with mainly ethanoate groups will
  be soluble or not. *In this question, 1 mark is for QWC.* (7 marks)

(e) Suggest one use for poly(ethenol) film. (1 mark)

Total: 15 marks

Answer to Question 2

(a)

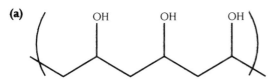

There is **1** mark for the correct number of carbon atoms and **1** mark for correctly positioned OH groups. Many students lose the second mark in drawing formulae by connecting the middle of the OH group, or even the hydrogen atom, to the carbon framework.

(b)

Note the words 'full structural formula' in the question. You must not write the methyl group as $-CH_3$.

(c) Addition ✓

Many students make the mistake of writing 'additional'!

(d) (i)

There is **1** mark for the correct shape of the water molecule. Beware: you would be surprised at the number of students in examinations who write it with two oxygen atoms and one hydrogen atom. There is **1** mark for the hydrogen bond being correct. Try to remember to line up the OH group, interaction and lone pair (it is not necessary to show the electrons) on the oxygen atom. The hydrogen bond is directional. The final mark is for correct use of partial charges.

(ii) There is extensive hydrogen bonding between chains in pure poly(ethenol) ✓, so the intermolecular forces are very strong ✓. Too much energy is needed to separate the chains ✓. Replacing a few OH groups by ethanoate groups disrupts the hydrogen bonding ✓. As the number of ethanoate groups increases, the strength of the intermolecular forces decreases ✓. The polymer dissolves because the OH groups in the chains can now hydrogen-bond to water ✓. If there are many ethanoate groups, then hydrogen bonding will be much less extensive and the polymer will be insoluble ✓.

There are seven marking points but only **6** marks available. The first two points and the final point must be given, for **3** marks. Then any three of the remaining four marking points score **1** mark each. The key intermolecular force in determining solubility is hydrogen bonding between polymer chains and water molecules. However, since hydrogen bonds have similar energies, it is important to focus on the *extent* of this bonding in deciding the strength of the overall intermolecular forces. There is no need to mention other types of intermolecular force, since these are much weaker than hydrogen bonding. The last marking point must be addressed in response to the question asked in the stem. The QWC mark requires the correct use of two of the following ideas:

- extent of hydrogen bonding
- intermolecular forces
- strength of hydrogen bonding

(e) Bags for washing contaminated hospital laundry ✓.

In this example, sealed bags containing contaminated laundry can be placed directly into the washing appliance. Other acceptable answers are coatings for capsules containing medicines for slow release and coatings for seeds to protect them from disease and decay.

■ ■ ■

(3) **Polymers that conduct electricity can be made from ethyne. Ethyne is an unsaturated compound containing a carbon–carbon triple bond. The triple bond reacts in a similar way to the carbon–carbon double bond in ethene.**

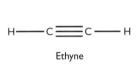

Ethyne

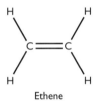

Ethene

(a) Bromine can react with ethyne to form two different unsaturated compounds. Both compounds have the same structural formula.

(i) **Draw this structural formula.** (1 mark)

(ii) **Explain how and why two isomers can have this structural formula.** (2 marks)

(iii) **Name this type of isomerism.** (1 mark)

(iv) **Give the colour change that occurs when ethyne is bubbled through dilute aqueous bromine.** (2 marks)

(b) (i) **Explain why bromine molecules are attracted to unsaturated molecules like ethene and ethyne.** (2 marks)

(ii) **The reaction between ethene and bromine takes place in two steps. Draw the structure of the intermediate carbocation formed in the first step.** (2 marks)

(iii) **Classify the mechanism for the reaction of bromine with ethene by choosing two words from the following:**

- **addition**
- **electrophilic**
- **elimination**
- **nucleophilic**
- **radical**
- **substitution** (2 marks)

(c) Polymers made from alkynes can form films that are flexible. Explain, in terms of intermolecular forces and the behaviour of polymer chains, why such polymers are flexible. (2 marks)

(d) Some of these polymers are called copolymers. Explain what this means. (1 mark)

Total: 15 marks

Answer to Question 3

(a) (i)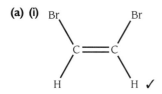

Structural formulae show the order of the bonds. If your structure has the name 1,2-dibromoethene, it is correct. Therefore, the *trans* isomer is also correct.

(ii) The two bromine atoms can be on the *same side* or on *opposite sides* of the C=C ✓. At room temperature, this bond *cannot rotate*, so the two compounds are isomers ✓.

The key words required are given in italics. There is no need to label the two different isomers or even draw them, although diagrams will answer the 'how' part of the question and gain the mark.

(iii) *cis–trans* ✓

Geometric would also gain the mark.

(iv) Orange ✓ to colourless ✓

Many students only gain 1 mark here. Either they confuse colourless and clear or state that 'bromine is decolourised'. Clear is about transparency — all coloured solutions are clear.

(b) (i) As a bromine molecule approaches a C=C, it is polarised by the electron-rich bond ✓. The nearer bromine atom is slightly positive and attacks the electron pair of one of the bonds ✓.

🄔 This is a hard question. It requires a clear understanding of electrophilic addition. The first mark is for making it clear that it is the double bond that causes the bromine molecule (not atom) to become polarised. The second mark is for indicating that the nearer bromine atom in the molecule then acts as an electrophile. There are several ways to make this second point, including the use of the term 'electrophile' or 'electrophilic'. Many students make the mistake of using the term electronegativity in referring to the C=C in this context.

(ii)

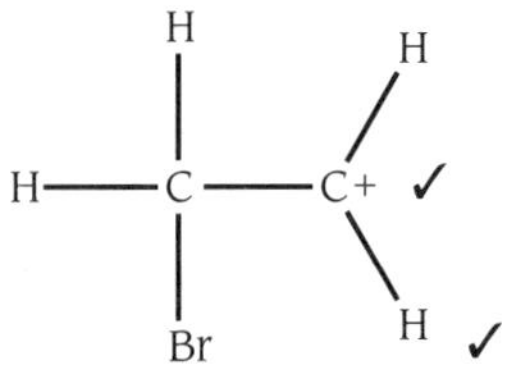

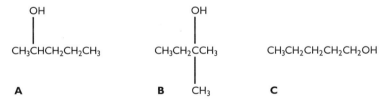

There is 1 mark for the correct structure and 1 mark for the correctly located positive charge. It is best to draw the full structure, since it is easy to check that the type and number of bonds are correct. The charge is usually omitted by students. However, you should note that 2 marks are allocated in the question.

(iii) Electrophilic ✓ addition ✓

Lists are usually given in alphabetical order. Note that three of the words are types of reaction and three are types of attacking species, so remember to choose one from each group. The previous parts of the question should have helped to jog your memory here.

(c) The intermolecular forces between polymer chains are instantaneous dipole–induced dipole forces, which are relatively weak ✓. The polymer chains are able to slide over one another ✓.

You need to focus on the causes of flexibility in polymers (see page 39). The first mark is for describing the intermolecular forces as weak — not for naming their type. You are not asked specifically to name them.

(d) The polymer is formed from more than one type of monomer ✓.

■ ■ ■

(4) Fusel oil is a liquid formed by the distillation of fermented potatoes. It is a mixture, mainly of alcohols. Three of these alcohols are compounds A, B and C, which all have the same molecular formula, $C_5H_{11}OH$. The structures of the alcohols are shown below.

OH
|
$CH_3CHCH_2CH_2CH_3$

A

OH
|
$CH_3CH_2CCH_3$
|
B CH_3

$CH_3CH_2CH_2CH_2CH_2OH$

C

(a) (i) State which of A, B and C is a secondary alcohol. Give your reasoning. (2 marks)
(ii) Give the reagent used for oxidising alcohols. (2 marks)
(iii) Give the structural formulae of the organic products, if any, which would form when each alcohol is oxidised. (4 marks)

(b) The boiling point of alcohol **B** is **102°C**, whereas that of **C** is **138°C**.
   (i) Name the strongest intermolecular force present in both **B** and **C**.   (2 marks)
   (ii) Explain the difference in the boiling points.   (5 marks)

Total: 15 marks

Answer to Question 4

(a) (i) A ✓ because there is only one H attached to the same C as the OH.

Stating that the OH group is on a C in the middle of the chain would also be worth the second mark.

(ii) Acidified ✓ potassium dichromate solution ✓

The question does not say 'name', therefore formulae are acceptable. The formulae may be given as ions, $H^+/Cr_2O_7^{2-}$. The acid may be specified by name, for example sulphuric acid.

(iii)

A

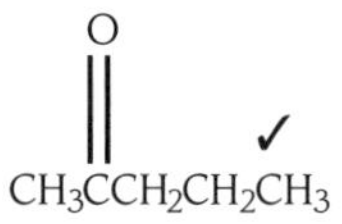

O

$CH_3CCH_2CH_2CH_3$ ✓

B

No product ✓

C

$CH_3CH_2CH_2CH_2C\overset{O}{\diagdown}_H$ ✓

$CH_3CH_2CH_2CH_2C\overset{O}{\diagdown}_{OH}$ ✓

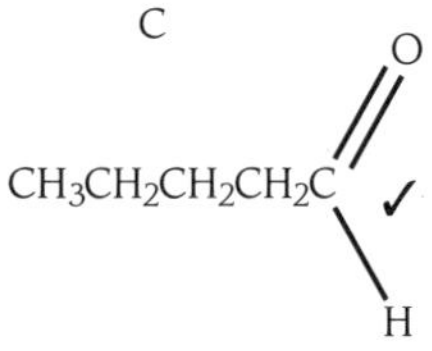

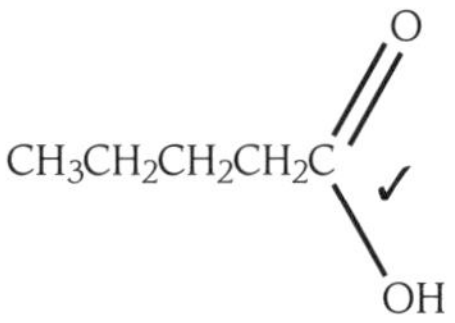

There is 1 mark each for A and B, and 1 mark each for the two C structures. The type of formulae used must distinguish between the three functional groups.

(b) (i) Hydrogen bonding ✓
   (ii) More energy is needed to separate the molecules in C than in B ✓. Therefore, the intermolecular forces in C must be greater than those in B ✓. Both B and C have instantaneous dipole–induced dipole forces ✓, but because B is a more compact ✓ molecule, these forces are lower in B than in C ✓.

The hydrogen bonding is similar in each case and so it is the weaker forces that are making the difference. Many students forget in this type of question to link boiling (or melting) point to the energy needed to separate the particles.